Optics in the Air

Observing Optical Phenomena through Airplane Windows

Optics in the Air
Observing Optical Phenomena through Airplane Windows

Joseph A. Shaw

SPIE PRESS
Bellingham, Washington USA

Library of Congress Cataloging-in-Publication Data

Names: Shaw, Joseph A., author.
Title: Optics through airplane windows / Joseph A. Shaw.
Description: Bellingham, Washington : SPIE Press, [2017] | Includes bibliographical references and index.
Identifiers: LCCN 2016046293 (print) | LCCN 2016050554 (ebook) | ISBN 9781510607293 (softcover) | ISBN 1510607293 (softcover) | ISBN 9781510607316 (epub) | ISBN 9781510607309 (pdf) | ISBN 9781510607323 (mobi)
Subjects: LCSH: Meteorological optics.
Classification: LCC QC975.2 .S53 2017 (print) | LCC QC975.2 (ebook) | DDC 551.56/5--dc23
LC record available at https://lccn.loc.gov/2016046293

Published by
SPIE
P.O. Box 10
Bellingham, Washington 98227-0010 USA
Phone: +1 360.676.3290
Fax: +1 360.647.1445
Email: books@spie.org
Web: http://spie.org

Printed in the United States of America.
First Printing.
For updates to this book, visit http://spie.org and type "PM274" in the search field.

Table of Contents

Preface

This book is a result of curiosity about the optical world around us. I have always found the natural optical world interesting, and this interest was nurtured by my scientist father, who would take young me outside at night to see the rings of Saturn or to photograph the aurora, and who taught me by example through his constant experimenting. One way or the other, I had to be affected by growing up in a home where everyday life included the house getting cold because my father had turned off the furnace in the middle of the Alaskan winter night so that he could better measure the gravitational field of a grapefruit in his basement laboratory!

The lessons at home were followed by my own professional experiences of curiosity-driven learning. For example, as an undergraduate student at the University of Alaska I worked as an assistant for a Japanese film crew who made the world's first color video of the aurora. I spent hours being taught by the American engineer how a video camera works while the Japanese engineer taught me the Japanese vocabulary so I could serve as interpreter in a discussion of how the Japanese camera worked and how the Alaskan scientists could get one of their own. Growing up under the aurora was a special treat!

Later, when I was a Ph.D. student studying optical sciences at the University of Arizona, I remember being frustrated one evening when I realized I could not clearly explain the source of the beautiful colors I was seeing in a cloud while I waited at a bus stop near the university. I remember vowing right then to learn everything possible about natural optical phenomena so that I could understand and help others understand the optical beauty visible to all who learn to look and see. This vow led me to carefully study a book on this topic, written by Aden and Marjorie Meinel. Aden was the founding director of the Optical Sciences Center where I was a Ph.D. student, and I appreciate his kind response to my letter thanking him for his wonderful book. This was followed with books by Robert Greenler and Marcel Minnaert, and later with books by David Lynch and William Livingston, Syun Akasofu, and others. As my library and understanding grew, so did my collection of photographs. It was my love of photography that led me to study optics in the first place, so this was a natural evolution. Soon I was carrying a camera everywhere I went, meeting with the "light and color in the open air" community every few years, and traveling the world to share my photographs and their explanations with everyone from elementary school students looking in awe at my photographs of the aurora to graduate students and optics professionals who wanted to learn more about this inspiring field.

Because I travel the world for research and presentations, my collection grew to include more and more photographs taken from airplanes. I eventually realized this was a fitting niche for my own book, which I now offer with the hope that it might help inspire others to better see, appreciate, and understand the optical world.

This book would not exist without the contributions of many people and organizations. It is my sincere pleasure to acknowledge and thank my colleagues and friends in the "light and color in the open air" community for teaching, inspiring, and encouraging me: specifically, Michael Vollmer, Kathy Creath, and Stan Gedzelman for reading and helping improve chapters; Les Cowley for helping me identify and better understand some of the phenomena in my photographs; and Robert Greenler for graciously encouraging me in this project. The book is much better because of their help, but any flaws are still my own.

I offer my sincere thanks to Montana State University for allowing me to take a sabbatical leave, which gave me the crucial time to sort and edit photographs and write most of this book. I greatly appreciate Jed Hancock and the Space Dynamics Laboratory at Utah State University in Logan, Utah, and Kazuhiko Oka and Hokkaido University in Sapporo, Japan, for hosting my sabbatical stay; Paul Nugent for helping run my research lab during this time; and all of my students for being patient with me while I was away.

Among the many who have helped in some way, I also wish to thank the publishing team at SPIE for helping turn my idea into reality, Blake Lerner and Boeing Co. for providing information about the construction of airplane windows, and the following people who let me use their photographs to beautifully fill gaps in my own collection: Michael Vollmer, Paul Neiman, Daniel Adams, Glenn Shaw, Brad Hudson, Claudia Hinz, Brad Lee Hudson, and Dan McGlaun.

Finally, I gratefully acknowledge my parents, Glenn and Gladys Shaw, for teaching me to see the world scientifically but appreciate it spiritually and artistically; my wife, Margaret, for being by my side and giving it all meaning; and my children, Aaron, Brian, and Amy, for their constant encouragement and support. I cannot imagine completing this project without their love and help.

Joseph Shaw
Bozeman, Montana
December 2016

Glossary

Alexander's dark band: a light-depleted region of the sky between a primary and secondary rainbow.

Anti-crepuscular rays (see also crepuscular rays): crepuscular rays extending to the anti-solar point on the horizon opposite the (usually rising or setting) sun.

Anti-solar point: the point opposite the sun, found by extending an imagery line from the sun through the observer's head and toward infinity, i.e., the location of the shadow of an observer's head.

Anti-twilight: The region of the sky, opposite the sun, lit by sunlight scattered in the atmosphere after sunset or before sunrise.

Aurora: A high-latitude optical display of usually green, red, or purple light in a dark sky, created when energetic particles from the sun collide with atoms and molecules at the top of the earth's atmosphere. Aurora Borealis is the effect seen in the northern hemisphere (often called the Northern Lights), and Aurora Australis is the same effect seen in the southern hemisphere.

Belt of Venus (also called the anti-twilight arch or twilight wedge): a region of usually pink light, often seen above the earth's shadow, on the opposite horizon from the setting or rising sun.

Bottlinger's rings: A rare and not-fully-explained elliptical halo surrounding a subsun.

Brocken spectre: the triangular shadow of an observer, stretched into fog or mist below the observer (usually seen from a mountain location).

Circumhorizontal arc (CHA): an ice-crystal halo effect seen as a colored band stretching partway around the horizon at a constant elevation angle low in the sky when the sun is high in the sky. See also circumzenithal arc.

Circumscribed halo: an ice halo effect seen as a distorted circle lying just outside of a 22° halo; the lower and upper tangent arcs merge to create this halo when the sun is higher than about 29° above the horizon.

Circumzenithal arc (CZA): an ice-crystal halo effect seen as a colored band stretching partway around the horizon at a constant elevation angle high in the sky when the sun is low in the sky. See also circumzenithal arc.

Cloudbow: a large, nearly colorless circle of light (or portion of a circle) centered on the anti-solar point, created by light refracted and reflected within tiny cloud droplets. Similar to a rainbow, but its colors are washed out by diffraction in the tiny droplets. See also fogbow.

Contrail: a long cloud streak formed by airplane exhaust condensing in cold air.

Corona: small concentric circles of colored light centered on the sun or other light source, created by diffraction (near-forward scattering) of light by tiny water droplets or ice particles in clouds or fog.

Crepuscular rays: rays of scattered light passing through gaps between clouds extending upward or downward from the usually rising or setting sun.

Earth's shadow: a dark band caused by the edge of the earth obstructing direct solar illumination of the opposite horizon from the setting or rising sun. See also Belt of Venus.

Eclipse: an astronomical event in which the moon blocks direct sunlight from illuminating a region on the earth (solar eclipse) or the earth blocks direct sunlight from illuminating the moon (lunar eclipse).

Fogbow: a large, nearly colorless circle of light (or portion of a circle) centered on the anti-solar point, created by light refracted and reflected within tiny fog droplets. Similar to a rainbow, but its colors are washed out by diffraction in the tiny droplets. See also cloudbow.

Glints: individual mirror-like reflections of a light source (such as the sun or moon) from a properly oriented surface such as water or ice.

Glitter: a collection of glints from randomly oriented surfaces, such as tiny capillary waves on water or ice crystals in the air (often called a glitter pattern, glitter path, or glitter patch on water or a sun or light pillar from ice crystals).

Glory: a small set of colored rings centered on the anti-solar or shadow point, caused by light from the sun (or other light source) scattering in near-backward directions that vary with wavelength (sometimes called anti-corona).

Green flash: a momentarily vivid green light seen as the last rim of the sun sets below the horizon (or as the first rim of the sun rises).

Halo: a pattern of light created in the sky by refraction and reflection in airborne ice crystals.

Heiligenschein: a bright region surrounding the shadow of an observer on a surface containing water drops, such as dew-moistened grass. See also opposition effect.

Infralateral arc: a halo arc formed below the sun or other light source by refraction in ice crystals where two surfaces meet to form a 90° angle, positioned near a rare 46° halo circle. See also supralateral arc.

Iridescence: spatially varying patterns of pastel colors caused by diffraction in clouds from tiny water droplets or ice particles that have locally uniform sizes that vary throughout the cloud.

Light loops: rings or distorted rings of light from the sky or nearby surroundings reflected from a lightly undulating water surface.

Light pillar: a vertically extended pattern of glints from ice crystals with random tilts; the ice-crystal reflection equivalent of a glitter pattern on wind-rippled water. See also sun pillar.

Midnight sun: literally, the sun remains above the horizon in the middle of the night at high-latitude locations in summer. More generally, a high-latitude night sky that never becomes dark because of the sun barely setting below the horizon and then rising again.

Noctilucent clouds (NLCs): thin, extremely-high-altitude clouds that are visible only when the sun is below the horizon so that the lower atmosphere is in shadow, with sunlight illuminating only the high clouds (noctilucent means "night-shining"). A high-latitude phenomenon visible as wispy, electric-blue clouds visible long after sunset or before sunrise.

Opposition effect: a phenomenon leading to a bright region surrounding an observer's shadow on a rough surface. See also heiligenschein.

Parhelion: a bright spot of light, often with a reddish inner edge and bluish outer edge, located approximately 22° to the left or right of the sun or moon and created by refraction in hexagonal ice crystals. See also sundog.

Rainbow: a large circle (or portion of a circle) of colored light centered on the anti-solar point, created by refraction and reflection within rain drops in the air (a primary bow undergoes one reflection within the water drops, and a secondary bow undergoes two reflections within the water drops. A double rainbow has simultaneously visible primary and secondary bows).

Scattering: the angular redirection of light interacting with a particle, with an angular pattern that depends on both the optical wavelength and particle size.

Scattering angle: the angle between the original trajectory and the new trajectory of scattered light. Look at the source to see the 0° scattering angle (forward), and look at the shadow point to see the 180° scattering angle (backward).

Scattering, backward: light scattered into directions nearly opposite the original trajectory. Look toward the anti-solar point to see backward-scattered sunlight.

Scattering, forward: light scattered into directions near the original trajectory. Look toward the light source to see forward-scattered light.

Scattering, Mie: a more sophisticated method of calculating scattering from spherical particles whose size may be smaller or larger than the wavelength.

Scattering, Rayleigh: a simple approximation that predicts a $1/\text{wavelength}^4$ dependence for scattered power, valid for particles much smaller than the wavelength.

Shadow: a region in space where an object blocks direct illumination by the sun or other light source.

Sparkles: often colored flashes of light arising from light refracted and reflected within ice crystals falling in the air or lying on the ground as snow.

Subparhelion: a parhelion or sundog located approximately 22° to the left or right of the subsun.

Subsun: a mirror-like reflection of the sun from ice crystals in calm air. The subsun elongates vertically into a subsun pillar with increased ice-crystal tilt angles.

Subsun pillar: a vertically elongated collection of sun reflections from ice crystals with random tilts.

Sun pillar: a vertically extended pattern of sun glints from ice crystals with different tilts. The ice-crystal reflection equivalent of a sun glitter pattern on wind-rippled water. See also light pillar.

Sundog: a bright spot of light, often with a reddish inner edge and bluish outer edge, located approximately 22° to the left or right of the sun or moon and created by refraction in airborne hexagonal ice crystals (see also parhelion).

Supernumerary bows: extra bows, arcs, or bands of light on the inside of a rainbow, cloudbow, or fogbow, created by interference of light scattered by the raindrops, cloud droplets, or fog droplets.

Supralateral arc: a halo arc formed above the sun or other light source by refraction in ice crystals where two surfaces meet to form a 90° angle, positioned near the rare 46° halo circle. See also infralateral arc.

Tangent arc (upper, lower): halo arcs positioned tangent to a circular halo. The upper and lower tangent arcs merge to form the circumscribed halo when the sun is higher than 29° above the horizon. See also circumscribed halo.

Twilight: the region of the sky lit by sunlight scattered in the atmosphere after sunset or before sunrise

Waves (water): periodic undulations of a water surface with a restorative force based on gravity (gravity waves) or surface tension (wind-driven capillary waves), or undulations within the water (internal waves).

Chapter 1
Introduction

1.1 Purpose and Scope

This book is about learning to see. Specifically, it is about learning to see the rich array of colors and optical effects that occur in nature and can be seen by an informed and alert passenger in an airplane. I hope to make your travel time more exciting and also to help you learn a little bit about the optical world that surrounds us. Most naturally occurring optical displays can be seen from an airplane, and some are even best seen in the air. However, your ability to appreciate and recognize optical phenomena will be enhanced if you know where and when to look and what to expect.

In this spirit of learning to see and understand, the primary objectives of this book are to (a) show examples of what can be seen from an airplane and (b) provide simple explanations to motivate and inform you about how to observe light and color in nature. This book expands upon earlier papers by Shaw[1] and others,[2] and an earlier book by Wood.[3] More advanced details about the science of each phenomenon can be gathered from Les Cowley's *Atmospheric Optics* website,[4] multiple books,[5–21] and articles from the feature journal issues[22–32] produced after each international conference on light and color in nature (held approximately every three years).[33,34]

1.2 Observation and Photography Tips

1.2.1 Where and when to look

Watching the sky is best done from a window seat. I plan my seat based on what I think might be observable on a given flight, given its primary travel direction, time of day, and season. For example, in the northern hemisphere, a seat on the left side of the plane (as seen by a forward-looking passenger) provides a view toward the morning sun and away from the afternoon sun on a north–south flight. A sun-side seat is ideal for enjoying the colors of sunrise, sunset, and twilight. Additionally, as shown in Fig. 1.1, a sun-side seat provides an opportunity to see halos, coronas, iridescence, crepuscular rays, glitter patterns on water, and so forth—but please do not look directly at the sun.

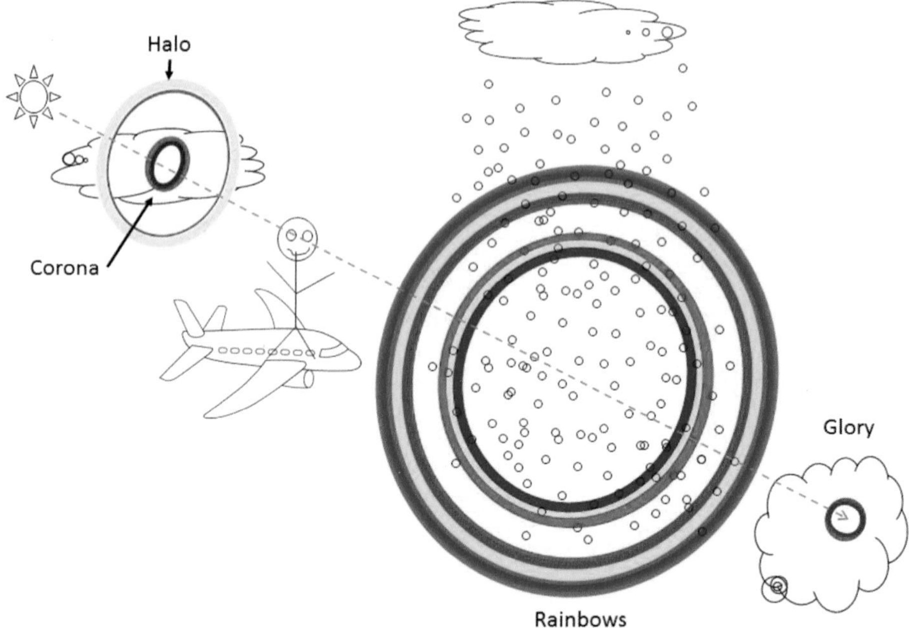

Figure 1.1 Some optical effects that might be seen during an airplane flight.

A seat on the shaded side is suitable for seeing glories, rainbows, cloudbows, the earth's shadow, cloud shadows, contrail shadows, anti-crepuscular rays, anti-twilight colors, moon rise, and so forth. On high-latitude flights, such as some trans-oceanic flights or flights to and from Alaska, I choose a seat on the side that provides the best view of the northern sky (or southern sky in the southern hemisphere), which is where auroras can be seen in a dark sky. It is also where noctilucent clouds may appear in a dark sky during summer. Of course, beautiful colors or interesting scenery may be visible on either side of the airplane at any time. Online seat maps and forums can help you avoid reserving a "window" seat with no window or a window seat with a view obstructed by a wing or engine.

1.2.2 Photography tips

The most important observation technique is to punctuate your work or reading with frequent, careful looks out the window, especially during takeoff and landing when the plane is most likely to pass through clouds. Photographing optical displays through an airplane window is best done with manual focus and sometimes manual exposure. A digital single-lens reflex (SLR) camera is ideal, but most daytime optical displays can be photographed with a high-quality phone camera or point-and-shoot camera. Regardless of what camera you use, be sure to turn off the flash and focus at infinity by using manual controls, "scenery" mode, or "airplane photo" mode. Failure to do so will result in pictures of a flash-obliterated airplane window or its scratches.

Once situated in my airplane seat, I wipe nose prints and smudges off the window, e.g., with one of the small napkins provided by the airline. Next, I examine the window to find the least-scratched area. I adjust the settings on my camera and place it either in my lap or next to my feet. I hold it in my hands while ascending or descending through clouds because optical displays pass by very quickly when seen from a fast-flying airplane.

Unless you have more influence with your pilot than I do with most, the airplane position is unlikely to be optimal for watching or photographing some optical effects. You may need to lean forward or back or hold the camera at unorthodox positions; accept that a non-level horizon and sub-optimal framing may occur because the optical display is rarely where you want it and the airplane may roll or turn.

Angles can be estimated surprisingly well with an outstretched arm: approximately 22° between an extended thumb and little finger (Fig. 1.2), 15° between index finger and little finger, 10° across your closed fist, 5° across your three middle fingers held together, and 1° across the short axis of your extended index finger. Extending your arm can be rather difficult in an airplane seat, but these are generally useful methods of estimating angles to quickly assess the size of colored rings or other optical displays.

Nighttime and low-light photography is always challenging, but an airplane is a uniquely challenging environment because of the numerous sources of interior light and the multiple window surfaces from which light can reflect. At the very least, use a free hand to minimize the amount of interior cabin light shining on the part of the window directly in front of your camera lens. You can also shade the window with a jacket or blanket over your head. I sometimes carry a jacket onto the plane when I would not otherwise simply because of the possibility of photographing difficult things such as the aurora. I also often strike up a conversation with people around me and with flight attendants to explain my intent before acting so out of the ordinary. Sometimes, if there is a nice aurora outside and my neighbor's reading light is causing me difficulty, I explain to them what I am doing and ask for their cooperation for a few minutes. Letting them see the photos on my camera screen usually helps.

As I mention later in the book, I have not found tripods to be very useful on airplanes because of the extremely limited space. I have used a monopod on occasion, but I worry about having it confiscated by airport security because of its club-like appearance. Furthermore, very long exposure times are not practical because even on a smooth flight the airplane is constantly vibrating and rocking from side to side, so stabilizing your camera with the airplane floor does not prevent blurred images. Instead, I usually shoot handheld photographs, even with exposure times as long as a few seconds in some cases. You can reduce the necessary exposure time by increasing the camera sensitivity with a higher ISO number, which has become very effective with digital SLR cameras in recent years (especially if you use a full-frame camera, as I do).

Figure 1.2 The angular distance between an extended thumb and little finger at arm's length is approximately 22°, illustrated here with a 22° halo.

Finally, consider including part of the wing or window mount in your shot to give context to your pictures. This is not always the best approach, or even possible, but it helps the viewer appreciate your location when you took the picture. This can often be achieved by using a wide-angle lens to capture the whole scene instead of just a spot of color or other detail. I find, for example, that I use my fisheye lens far more than a telephoto for photographing from airplanes. Regardless of what camera and lens you choose, or whether you take any pictures, don't forget to look—and enjoy what you are seeing!

1.2.3 Airplane-window optical effects

A commercial airplane window is not what you would like to place between your camera and a beautiful scene, but the lack of practical alternatives led me to a decision long ago to understand the window and consider it part of the "airplane scene." Sometimes the window adds interest to the scene (Fig. 1.3), but other times it simply adds inevitable imperfections or distractions (Fig. 1.4).

Some airplane windows are surprisingly badly scratched. Even an unscratched window, though, reduces the sharpness of photographs because its surfaces are extremely uneven relative to an optical wavelength (visible light wavelengths are 400 to 700 nm, or about one-half millionth of a meter). Consequently, zooming in to photograph details on the ground from a high-flying airplane does not work well. Cameras used for aerial photography look through windows that are much more expensive than what we get to look through.

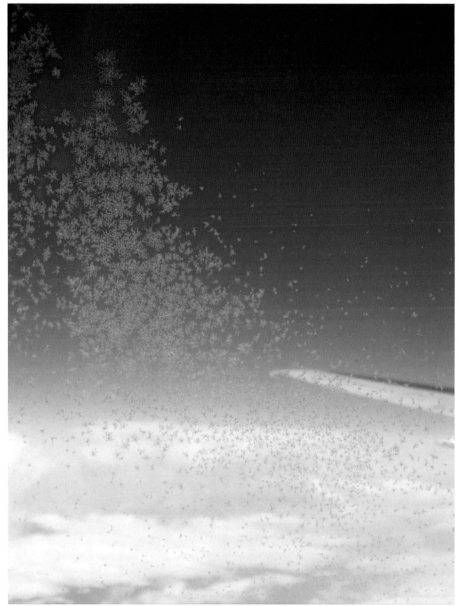

Figure 1.3 Ice crystals on an airplane window (MSP–MCO, 18 April 2006).

Although commercial airplane windows do not have high-quality optical surfaces, they are designed with some clever features. For example, most airplane windows have two thick panes of stretched acrylic, separated by an air gap and mounted in a pressure seal. The thickest outer pane is designed to withstand the large stress of cabin pressurization and is sometimes curved to match the external aircraft body. The middle pane has one or more breather holes to allow cabin air

(a)

(b)

Figure 1.4 Photographs showing the effect of window scratches when looking (a) toward the sun and (b) away from the sun (BZN–SLC, 29 Sep. 2013 and SLC–TUS, 5 Nov. 2013).

to reach the inner surface of the outer pane. Without this hole, moist air reaching the inner surface of the outer pane would condense on the window because the outside air at flight altitude is extremely cold (typically –40 to –60°C). The cold, dry outside air is pressurized and humidified before being released into the cabin, but it is still dry enough to prevent condensation on the cold outer window pane (as a result, you will find your skin to be notably dry after long flights). When boarding a plane, I sometimes find my window covered with condensation, but it then dries quickly as the plane climbs into drier air. Similarly, I frequently see increased window condensation or ice during a descent into more humid air (Fig. 1.3 is an example of this).

Finally, even a brief discussion of the optical effects of airplane windows would be incomplete without mentioning polarization, which describes the tendency of light waves to oscillate in a certain direction.[18,19] This phenomenon is significant because of the common use of polarized sunglasses and polarizing filters on camera lenses. The stretched acrylic material of the airplane window is birefringent, which means its stressed material bends and transmits light differently for light waves oscillating in different directions, i.e., light of different polarization states; furthermore, it does this differently for different colors. In fact, a well-known optical method of testing for material stress involves placing the material between two crossed polarizers, i.e., polarization filters with orthogonal transmission axes, and observing the resulting pattern of pastel colors. We cannot place a polarizer outside the window during flight, but nature takes care of that because light from the sky is partially polarized. Therefore, looking through an airplane window with polarized sunglasses or with a polarizing filter on a camera lens can produce dramatic colored patterns because of the "stress birefringence" in the window. This phenomenon is discussed in more detail in Chapter 10, but Fig. 1.5 shows a nice example. Because of this effect, you should not use a polarizing filter when photographing through an airplane window unless you are emphasizing a polarized scene (e.g., rainbow or cloudbow) and are willing to accept these colors, or unless you are purposely using these colors in your photograph for visual effect.

1.3 Organization of the Book

Each chapter of this book is devoted to a different type of natural optical phenomenon. If you are searching for the explanation of something you saw, refer to Fig. 1.1 to find something that roughly matches what you saw and where you saw it. For example, if you saw colored rings around the sun, the figure would guide you to look at the chapters on halos and coronas. Conversely, if you saw colored rings around the airplane shadow point, it would direct your attention to the chapters on rainbows and glories. These are all optical effects that can be seen by the eye, so the photographs are the centerpiece of the book. In addition to a brief description of what is shown in each photograph, each caption includes in parentheses the airport codes for the origin and destination of the flight on which it was taken. I hope this helps you visualize things more completely as you read.

Figure 1.5 Colors observed when photographing partially polarized skylight through a birefringent airplane window using a circularly polarizing filter on the camera lens. See Section 10.2 for further discussion (ANC–SEA, 14 Jan. 2016).

References

1. J. A. Shaw, "Observing light in nature from an airplane window," *Proc. SPIE* **7782**, 778208 (2010).
2. L. Larmore and F. F. Hall, Jr., "Optics for the airborne observer," *Opt. Eng.* **9**, 87–94 (1971).
3. E. A. Wood, *Science from Your Airplane Window*, Dover, New York (1975).
4. www.atoptics.co.uk
5. M. Minnaert, *The Nature of Light and Color in the Open Air*, Dover, New York (1954, English translation of original Dutch published in 1937).
6. M. Minnaert, *Light and Color in the Outdoors*, Springer, New York (1995, revised version with added color photographs).
7. R. Greenler, *Rainbows, Halos, and Glories*, Cambridge University Press, Cambridge (1980).
8. A. Meinel and M. Meinel, *Sunsets, Twilights, and Evening Skies*, Cambridge University Press, Cambridge (1991).
9. D. K. Lynch and W. Livingston, *Color and Light in Nature*, 3rd ed., Thule Scientific, Topanga, CA (2010).
10. W. Tape, *Atmospheric Halos*, Am. Geophys. Union, Washington, D.C. (1994).

11. W. Tape, *Atmospheric Halos and the Search for Angle X*, Am. Geophysical Union, Washington, DC (2006).
12. R. L. Lee, Jr. and A. B. Fraser, *The Rainbow Bridge: Rainbows in Art, Myth, and Science*, Penn State University Press, State College, PA (2001).
13. C. F. Bohren, *Clouds in a Glass of Beer*, Dover, New York (2001).
14. C. F. Bohren, *What Light Through Yonder Window Breaks?*, Dover, New York (2006).
15. N. Bone, *Aurora: Observing and Recording Nature's Spectacular Light Show*, Springer, New York (2010).
16. N. Davis, *Aurora Watcher's Handbook*, University of Alaska Press (1992).
17. S. I. Akasofu, *The Northern Lights: Secrets of the Aurora Borealis*, Alaska Northwest Books (2009).
18. G. P. Können, *Polarized Light in Nature*, Cambridge University Press, Cambridge (1985).
19. K. L. Coulson, *Polarization and Intensity of Light in the Atmosphere*, A. Deepak Publishing, Hampton, VA (1988).
20. J. Naylor, *Out of the Blue*, Cambridge University Press, Cambridge (2002).
21. J. Adam, *A Mathematical Nature Walk*, Princeton University Press, Princeton (2009).
22. D. L. Coffeen, "Polarization and scattering characteristics in the atmospheres of Earth, Venus, and Jupiter," *J. Opt. Soc. Am.* **69**(8), 1051–1198 (1979).
23. *J. Opt. Soc. Am.* **73**(12), 1622–1664 (1983).
24. *J. Opt. Soc. Am. A* **4**(3), 558–620 (1987).
25. *Appl. Opt.* **30**(24), 3381–3552 (1991).
26. *Appl. Opt.* **33**(21), 4535–4760 (1994).
27. *Appl. Opt.* **37**(9), 1425–1588 (1998).
28. *Appl. Opt.* **42**(3), 307–525 (2003).
29. *Appl. Opt.* **44**(27), 5623–5762 (2005).
30. *Appl. Opt.* **47**(34), LC1–LC2; H1–H224 (2008).
31. *Appl. Opt.* **50**(28), LC1–LC2, F1–F171 (2011).
32. *Appl. Opt.* **54**(4), LC1–LC2, B1–B265 (2015).
33. R. G. Greenler and D. K. Lynch, "Light and color in nature: A return to optics' roots," *Opt. Photonics News* **22**(9), 30–37 (2011).
34. www.lightandcolorinnature.org

Chapter 2
Sky Colors

2.1 Clear Sky Colors

The easiest optical effect to observe through an airplane window is the variation of sky color from the hazy, particle-laden lower atmosphere to the clear blue sky at flight altitude. This transition is particularly striking when leaving humid or hazy air, as illustrated in Fig. 2.1. This fisheye photograph was taken through an airplane window shortly after leaving Washington, D.C., and it shows that the hazy lower atmosphere gives way to a rich blue sky above the high-altitude cirrus clouds (it also includes an interesting example of cloud shadows in the haze). The blue skylight is a result of scattering by atmospheric gas molecules (primarily nitrogen and oxygen). When the light encounters these gas molecules, it is scattered—or sent in a new direction—and this scattering by molecules much smaller than the wavelength occurs more readily for blue light than for red light, as shown in Fig 2.2. For these tiny molecules, the amount of scattered light is proportional to one over the fourth power of the wavelength ($1/\lambda^4$, where λ is the optical wavelength). This is called Rayleigh scattering, named for Lord Rayleigh, who in the late 1800s developed the theory for scattering that leads to a blue sky.

Actually, Rayleigh scattering alone is insufficient to account for the blue that we see in the sky. It only predicts more scattering of violet light than blue light, and more scattering of ultraviolet light than violet light. In fact, there are two primary reasons why we see a blue sky and not a violet (or ultraviolet) sky. First, the human eye sees violet light with lower sensitivity relative to blue light; second, ozone high in the atmosphere absorbs ultraviolet light before it reaches the lower atmosphere where we live and where airplanes fly (the ozone is located even higher than the top of the lower atmosphere, where airplanes fly for increased efficiency). When you combine these effects, you find that the skylight actually has a violet peak, but the skylight as perceived by humans has a blue peak.

Referring again to Fig. 2.1, haze in the lower atmosphere causes skylight there to be whitened because scattering by larger haze particles (called "aerosols") is much more constant with wavelength (or color) than Rayleigh scattering by tiny gas molecules. This phenomenon can be illustrated with the more sophisticated Mie scattering theory for spherical particles larger than the wavelength (see Section 2.6).[1–4]

Figure 2.1 Blue sky and white clouds above with aerosol haze and cloud shadows below (DCA–MSP, 20 June 2010).

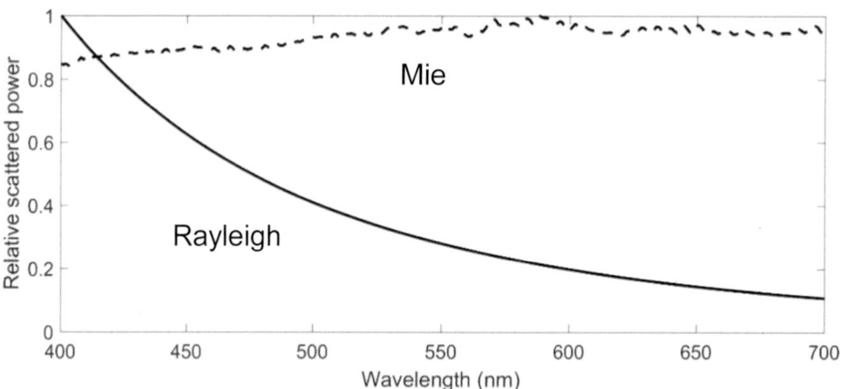

Figure 2.2 Wavelength dependence for Rayleigh scattering by gas molecules and Mie scattering by liquid water droplets (calculated using MiePlot[4] for the power scattered in the backward hemisphere for particle radii of 1 nm and 10 μm and plotted normalized to the peak value for each curve).

Figure 2.2 shows how the amount of scattered light varies with wavelength for "optically large" particles larger than the wavelength (dashed curve) and "optically small" particles much smaller than the wavelength (solid curve). The small change of the dashed curve tells us that light scattered by clouds or haze appears white or gray. Conversely, the constant decay of the solid curve indicates that light scattered by tiny gas molecules appears blue or violet.

Figure 2.3 Blue sky and white clouds with a nearly full moon in the daytime sky (SLC–BZN, 24 Oct. 2002).

In Fig. 2.3, the distinct difference between the blue sky and white clouds arises because of the vastly different sizes of atmospheric gas molecules and cloud droplets. This photograph also shows that the moon, when viewed high in the sky, is essentially as white as the cloud because the moon reflects all wavelengths nearly equally. Therefore, scattered moonlight produces the same sky colors as scattered sunlight. In fact, although the moonlit night sky appears dark to our eyes, it is actually just as blue as the daytime sky.[5]

In the scene of Fig. 2.4, lit by the full moon, the sky is blue and the scenery looks just as it did during daytime, but I took the photograph with a 148-s exposure, two hours after sunset. The Big Dipper sitting prominently above the mountains makes it more obvious that this is a nighttime image (the earth's rotation during the long exposure time caused the stars to become streaks). We do not see the blue sky at night with our eyes because we cannot collect light for several minutes, as a camera can. Scattered moonlight is about a half-million times darker than the sunlit sky,[5] which is not bright enough for reliable color vision.[6] At night we see with visual detectors called rods, which provide high sensitivity without color. Another set of visual detectors called cones provide color vision with lower sensitivity during the day.

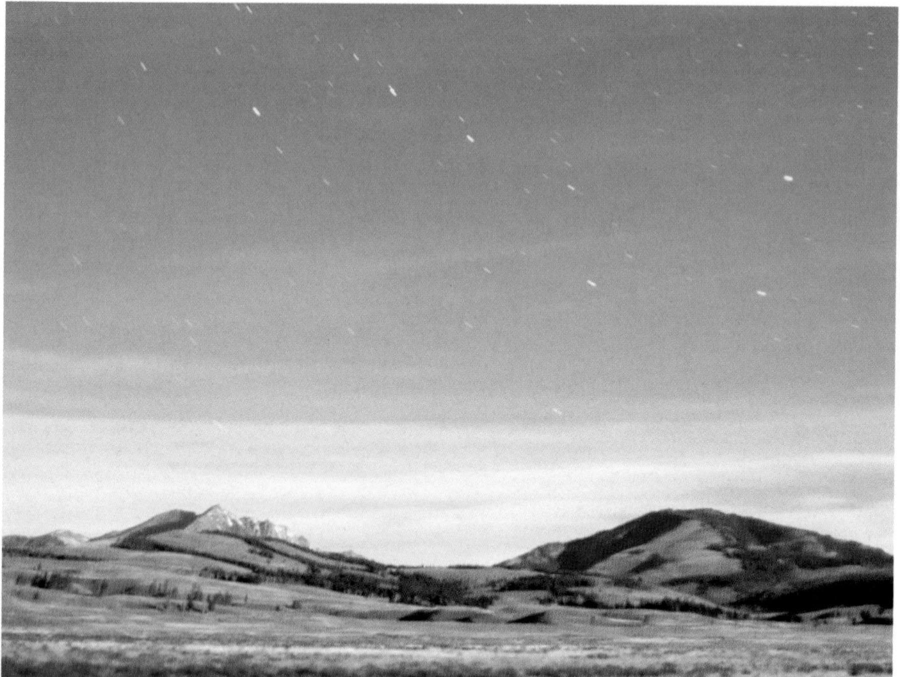

Figure 2.4 Long-exposure photograph showing the blue sky at night with the Big Dipper prominently visible (Yellowstone National Park, WY).

2.2 Sunrise and Sunset Colors

The same scattering process that creates the light-blue sky color in Fig. 2.1 is also responsible for the gradient from dark blue to flaming oranges and reds we see during sunrise and sunset (Fig. 2.5). Light from the low sun traverses an atmospheric path that is longer than usual, leading to increased depletion of blue light by scattering. For example, in Fig. 2.5 direct light from the sun and its immediate vicinity has become a vivid orange color by scattering in the long path through the dense lower atmosphere. Conversely, the tiny bit of sunlight reaching the higher atmosphere, where the air is thin and clean, is scattered to produce the dark-blue twilight colors in the middle and top of the image. The effect of atmospheric path length is illustrated further in Fig. 2.6, where observers on the western side of a country see a blue sky while observers on the east side of the same country watch a beautiful sunset featuring the red light that remains after the blue light was removed by scattering along the path from west to east.

Because cloud particles scatter light with very little wavelength dependence (Fig. 2.2), clouds essentially assume the color of whatever light illuminates them. I like to think of clouds as the canvas on which Mother Nature's colors are displayed. Clouds illuminated by a high sun look white (as in Fig. 2.1), but clouds illuminated by a low setting or rising sun look red or orange. For example, Fig. 2.7 is a red sunset I photographed on the runway at Burbank, California. The deep red color indicates that the sun was very low on the horizon,

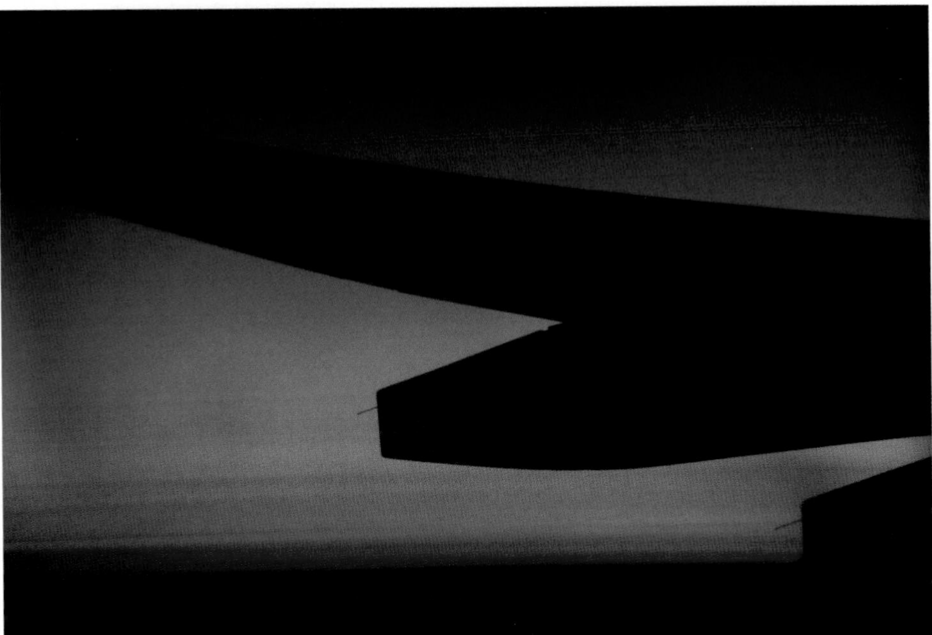

Figure 2.5 Colors of the twilight sky seen from high above southern Greenland (MSP–AMS, 27 May 2010).

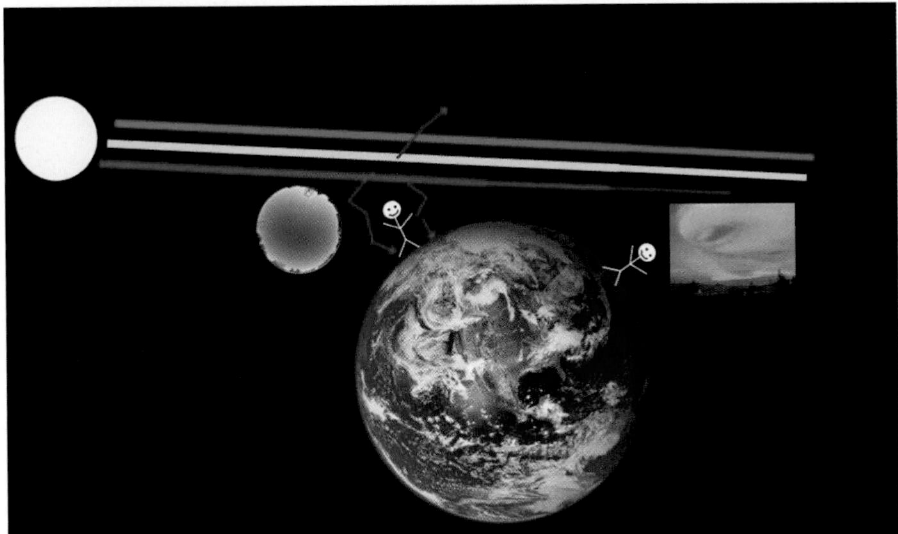

Figure 2.6 Rayleigh scattering by atmospheric gas molecules creates a blue sky in the west while the blue-depleted sunlight creates a red sunset in the east.

so the sunlight had traversed a long path through a particle-laden atmosphere, becoming completely depleted of blue light. A subtle pink color is seen on the tops of the clouds in the sunset photograph in Fig. 2.8. The colors of sunset and sunrise

Figure 2.7 Orange-red clouds lit by blue-depleted sunlight at sunset (BUR–SLC, 10 Dec. 2010).

Figure 2.8 Pink sunset light on cloud tops (BZN–SLC, 24 Sep. 2002).

change quickly because the atmospheric path length increases as the secant (1/cosine) of the sun angle from the zenith.[7] Like clouds, the moon is lit by the sun and reflects light with very little wavelength dependence, so it also assumes a rapidly evolving orange-red color when viewed through a long atmospheric path. Figure 2.9(a) is a rising orange moon I photographed on approach to Albuquerque, New Mexico. Figure 2.9(b) is a closer view of an orange moon. Figure 2.9(c) shows that similar effects occur for the rising or setting sun, e.g., a setting sun turned deep red because of scattering by thick wildfire smoke.

(a)

(b) (c)

Figure 2.9 Photos of (a) the moon rising over Albuquerque, New Mexico (SLC–ABQ, 3 Nov. 2015); (b) the moon rising over Bozeman, Montana; and (c) the sun viewed through dense wildfire smoke in Bozeman, Montana.

The anti-twilight sky opposite the sunset also becomes richly colored by scattering in a long atmospheric path. The early twilight sky often exhibits a pink band that is created by reddened light from the setting sun mixing with deep blue light on the eastern horizon. This pink band, called the anti-twilight arch or "Belt of Venus," rises from the eastern horizon as the sun sets in the west.[8] Once the sun has set, a dark band rises into the bottom of the pink band. This is the shadow of the earth on the distant horizon. Actually, the shadow can be seen even when the sun is above the horizon because rays from the shadow region are bent toward the observer by the atmosphere. Both the Belt of Venus and the earth's shadow are made visible by scattering from atmospheric gas molecules and aerosols, so the observed colors and brightness depend on what kind of particles are in the air. The best anti-twilight colors require clean air with few aerosols.[9,10]

The same anti-twilight sky transition is visible during sunrise but in the reverse order. In this case, the earth's shadow and Belt of Venus both set on the western horizon as the sun rises in the east. An example is shown in Fig. 2.10 with a sequence of photographs from a trans-Pacific flight. Because this flight was in January, the afternoon sun set as we followed the great-circle arc northwest from Amsterdam to Iceland, and it rose again as we continued southwest over eastern Canada to Minneapolis. In Fig. 2.10(a), the earth's shadow hugs the horizon while the sky higher up begins to brighten; in Fig. 2.10(b), the Belt of Venus is setting into the earth's shadow; and in Fig. 2.10(c), the shadow has set, the sun has risen, and the horizon is lit with pink and orange light that also illuminates the airplane engine. (The duration of twilight is prolonged by flying away from the rising sun or toward the setting sun, and shortened by flying in the opposite direction.)

Figure 2.11 shows pink light intruding into the earth's shadow from below. This might seem backward until you realize that in this case the pink light is scattering from the clouds located between the airplane and the distant horizon. Before the pink light could reach the distant horizon to form a Belt of Venus, it was intercepted by these cloud tops, and perspective makes it look like the nearby cloud tops are located below the horizon.

2.3 Scattering by Smoke and Air Pollution

The myriad of particles suspended in the air (aerosols) come from both natural and man-made sources. Aerosols exist with many sizes, but the ones that are most important for optically scattering have diameters comparable to or larger than the wavelength (0.5 μm and larger). A major source of aerosols in many regions of the world is wildfire smoke during dry summer months, and although this smoke is annoying it also can provide some interesting and even beautiful optical effects.

For example, notice in Fig. 2.12 that the mountains have a bluish cast that becomes progressively stronger with distance because of scattering in the air between the observer and the distant mountains. Figure 2.13 shows a more isolated layer of smoke that was seen most easily against the white clouds and mountain when the airplane ascended through the altitude of the layer.

In addition to wildfire smoke, many cities are often veiled in air pollution, which is sometimes trapped in stagnant air by a temperature inversion that prevents vertical mixing because the colder air lying above the warmer air traps pollution near the ground. This temperature profile is upside down (or inverted) from the more common condition in which air temperature decreases with altitude in the lower atmosphere. One of several possible causes of a temperature inversion is the ground cooling more rapidly than the air above. This happens most readily with dry air that is highly transparent to thermal infrared radiation escaping from the

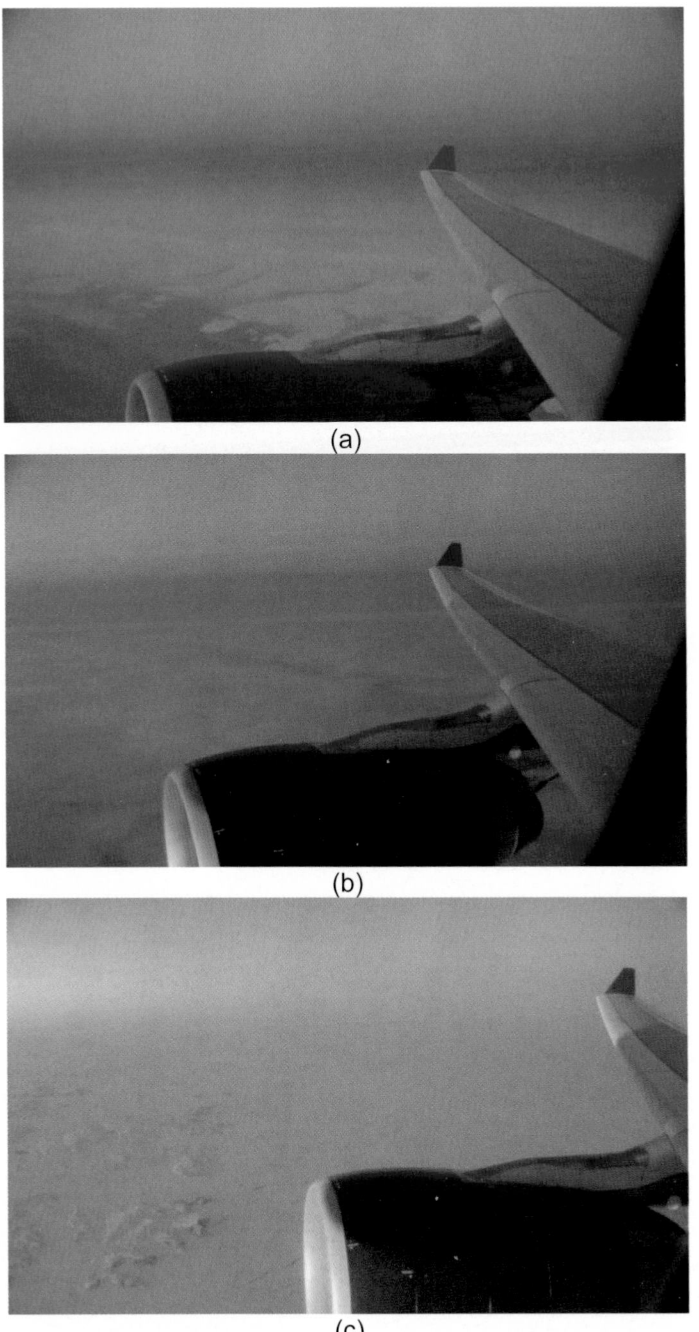

(a)

(b)

(c)

Figure 2.10 Photographs of twilight and Earth's shadow: (a) earth's shadow, (b) Belt of Venus setting into the shadow, and (c) pink and orange light of the rising sun (AMS–MSP, 11 Jan. 2014).

Figure 2.11 Pink light on clouds below the earth's shadow at sunset, looking eastward (SLC–BZN, 24 July 2004).

Figure 2.12 Photo of the Cascade Mountains in Washington State (USA) viewed through wildfire smoke (BZN–SEA, 27 July 2007).

Figure 2.13 Photograph of a smoke layer that became visible in front of clouds and Mt. Rainier as the airplane rose through the altitude of the smoke layer (SEA–OGG, 21 July 2010).

Figure 2.14 Photograph of air pollution trapped vertically by a temperature inversion and horizontally by the Wasatch Mountains (SEA–SLC, 11 Jan. 2010).

ground to space. Such conditions are common in cities at high altitudes and can be made worse by mountains trapping the air horizontally (e.g., Los Angeles, Mexico City, Salt Lake City), as illustrated in Fig. 2.14.

2.4 Skylight Angular Distribution

An interesting characteristic of Rayleigh scattering is the equal amounts of forward and backward scattering. That is, the light is equally likely to be scattered near its original direction of propagation or back toward the source. This principle can be seen in the all-sky photograph in Fig. 2.15(a) with very clean air. In this image, north is at the top, west is on the right, and the sun is behind the tree at the bottom left. The forward–backward symmetry is manifested by the nearly identical brightness and color of the sky near the sun on the bottom and on the opposite side.

Figure 2.15(b) is a similar photograph taken near the same location when the air contained some wildfire smoke. This time the sun was in the western sky on the right side, and there is a distinct brightness and color difference between the sky near the sun on the right side and the sky on the opposite (left) side. This difference occurs because the optically large smoke particles scatter more light in the forward direction than in the backward direction (recall that we see forward-scattered light near the sun and backward-scattered light in the sky opposite the sun). Increased forward scattering is a general result for optically large particles, although it is not at all intuitive from a geometric optics perspective!

Rather than crawling over people to illustrate this by taking pictures out of both sides of the plane, I found a nice opportunity one morning as my flight approached Seattle by flying north over Lake Washington and then turning around to land to the south. I took the photograph in Fig. 2.16(a) while I was looking west, and then a few seconds later I took the eastward-looking photograph in Fig. 2.16(b) as we turned to land to the south. It looks much hazier to the east, but this is actually a result of looking toward the sun and seeing all of the forward-scattered light. In reality, there are haze particles over the entire area, but the weak backward scattering from these particles causes the westward-viewing picture to look much clearer than the eastward-viewing picture.

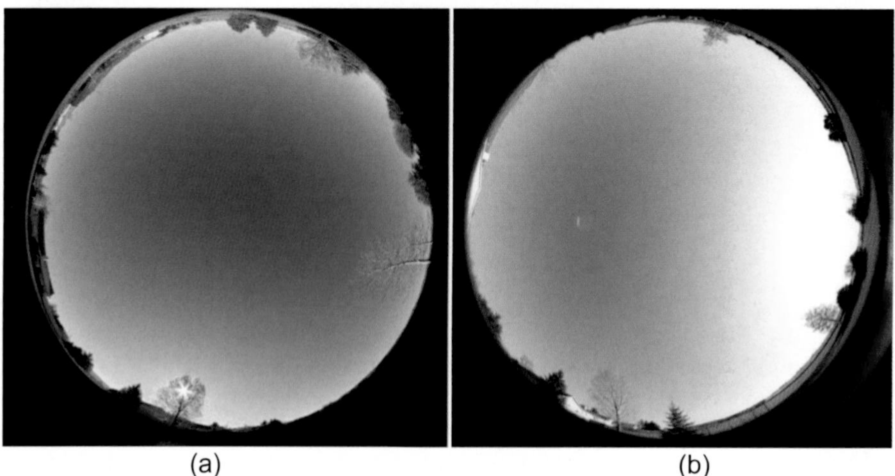

(a) (b)

Figure 2.15 All-sky photographs in (a) clean and (b) smoky air, illustrating enhanced aerosol scattering near the sun with smoke in the air (Bozeman, MT).

(a)

(b)

Figure 2.16 Photos demonstrating that haze particles scatter light preferentially in the forward direction: (a) looking across Lake Washington to the west, away from the sun, and (b) looking southeast across the lake with the sun just outside the left side of the picture (SLC–SEA, 10 June 2015).

2.5 The Green Flash

If you sit on a beach and watch the sunset, you will see the sun turn progressively more orange, then red, and, if you are lucky, your last glimpse will be of the top of the sun turning green very briefly before disappearing below the horizon. This phenomenon occurs because blue and green light are refracted (bent) in the atmosphere more than orange and red light, but the blue light is lost to scattering before it reaches your eye. For a green flash to be visible, the color-dependent bending must be enhanced by a mirage effect, e.g., when a layer of warm air exists over cooler water. The green flash is best seen when you are near the surface but still high enough that the warm air layer is below you.

Even though this classic explanation involves the sun setting into an ocean horizon, water is not required. A green flash can be seen anywhere with the required conditions, which exist frequently at the beach. A green flash also can be seen at sunrise if you look right when the top of the sun just emerges.

Several times I have seen a green flash from an airplane, once repeatedly while watching the sun "rise" and "set" behind mountains as my plane descended into Salt Lake City. I was fortunate to get a picture quickly before the fast-flying plane caused the already short-lived flash to disappear even more rapidly than if I was on a beach. The full image [Fig. 2.17(a)] was recorded with a wide-angle lens because that is what I had at the time. A cropped image [Fig. 2.17(b)] emphasizes the green flash. I suspect that a common winter-temperature inversion in the Salt Lake Valley provided the elevated warm layer and that my observing position was sufficiently low because the airplane was landing.

A more dramatic green flash is shown in Fig. 2.18, a photograph taken by my father[17] in Fairbanks, Alaska. I recall that when I was a young boy there was a period of time when we took dinner to him each night at an overlook where he was observing and photographing the green flash. From those observations he published one of the seminal papers on the phenomenon.[18]

2.6 Mie Scattering from Rain Drops and Cloud Droplets

All of the topics discussed in this chapter and the next three chapters arise from optical scattering and can be explored using a Mie scattering code for spherical particles (Rayleigh scattering is incorporated into Mie scattering). Figure 2.19 shows how light is scattered as a function of angle for optically large rain drops (top) and smaller water cloud or fog droplets (bottom). These plots show where to see four optical phenomena discussed in this book: coronas, rainbows, cloudbows, and glories. Figure 2.19(a) is for rain drops (radius = 3 mm) and Fig. 2.19(b) is for cloud droplets (radius = 0.01 mm or 10 μm). Both plots show the amount of scattered light versus scattering angle (the angle by which the scattered light is diverted). A 0° scattering angle means the light continues on its original trajectory and 180° means the light is redirected back toward its source. Light scattered near 0° ("forward scatter") is seen by looking in the vicinity of the sun. Light scattered near 180° ("backward scatter") is seen by looking toward the anti-solar point, or point opposite the sun (the eastern horizon when the sun sets in the west).

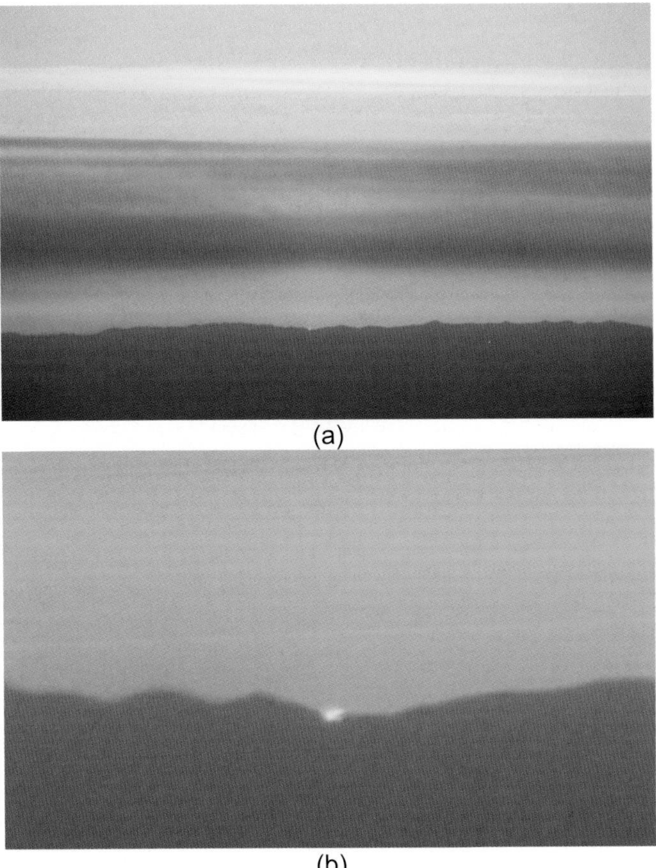

(a)

(b)

Figure 2.17 Green flash observed with the setting sun: (a) full image and (b) cropped segment emphasizing the green flash (BZN–SLC, 15 Feb. 2013).

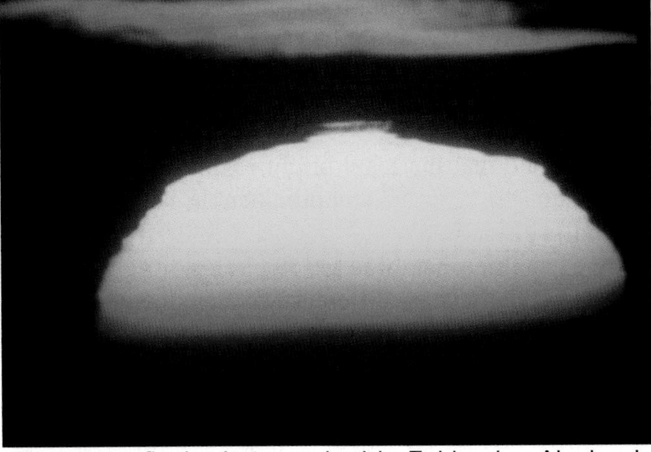

Figure 2.18 The green flash photographed in Fairbanks, Alaska. Image printed with permission from Glenn E. Shaw.

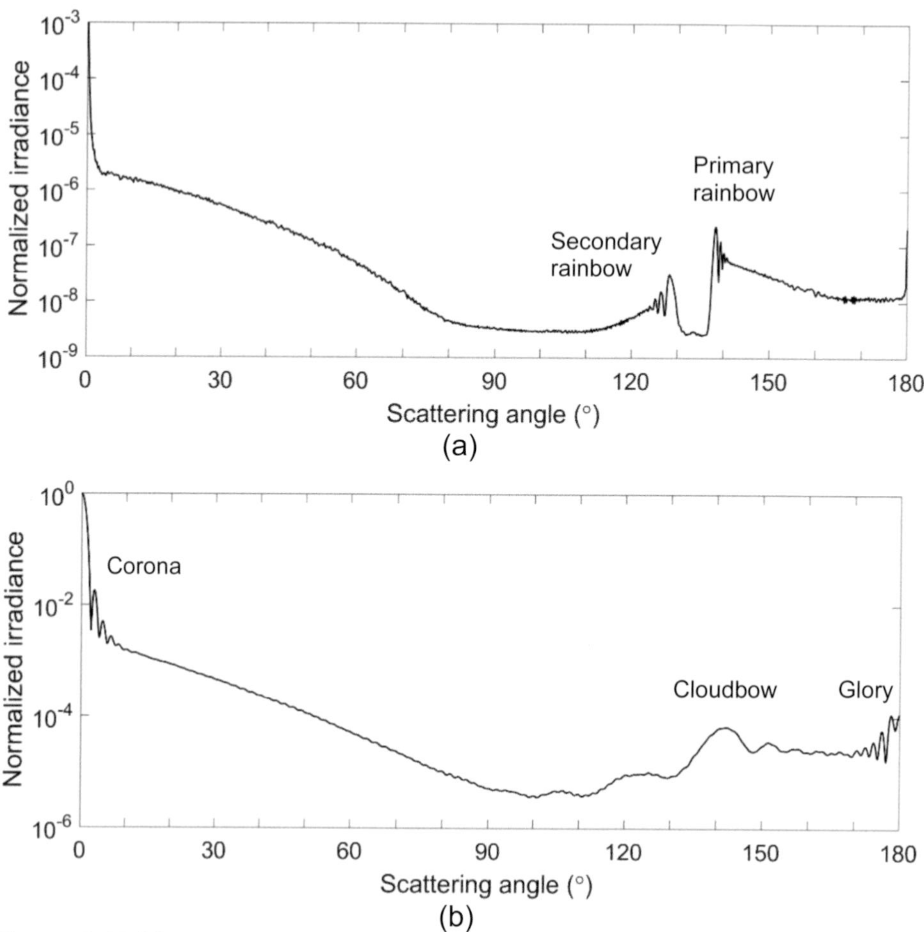

Figure 2.19 Mie scattering plots of the amount of scattered light as a function of the scattering angle for liquid water at a 650-nm wavelength: (a) raindrops with a lognormal size distribution of 0.3-mm mean radius and 5% standard deviation; (b) cloud droplets with a lognormal size distribution of 10-μm mean radius and 10% standard deviation. Calculated with MiePlot.[4]

These plots illustrate that there are bright regions of scattered light within a few degrees of the sun (the "corona"), approximately 129° and 138° from the sun (the secondary and primary rainbows), and near 180° from the sun (the glory). From symmetry we can infer that these are all circles of light, as suggested in Fig. 1.1. Repeating the calculations for different wavelengths would reveal the colors of these circles. Differences between the top and bottom plots suggest that when light is scattered by cloud droplets instead of rain drops, the rainbow becomes smoother with less color (a "cloudbow"). Each of these points is illustrated more completely in later chapters.

References

1. C. F. Bohren and D. R. Huffman, *Absorption and Scattering of Light by Small Particles*, Wiley, New York (1998).
2. C. F. Bohren and E. Clothiaux, *Fundamentals of Atmospheric Radiation*, Wiley-VCH, Berlin (2006).
3. P. Laven, "Simulation of rainbows, coronas and glories using Mie theory and the Debye series," *J. Quant. Spectrosc. Radiat. Transfer* **89**, 257–269 (2004).
4. www.philiplaven.com
5. J. A. Shaw, "The digital blue sky at night," *Opt. Photonics News* **16**(11), 18–23 (2005).
6. G. Smith, A. J. Vingrys, J. D. Maddocks, and C. P. Hely, "Color recognition and discrimination under full-moon light," *Appl. Opt.* **33**(21), 4741–4748 (1994).
7. M. Vollmer and S. Gedzelman, "Colors of the sun and moon: the role of the optical air mass," *Eur. J. Phys.* **27**, 299–309 (2006).
8. R. L. Lee, Jr., "Measuring and modeling twilight's Belt of Venus," *Appl. Opt.* **54**(4), B194–B203 (2015).
9. R. L. Lee, Jr., personal communication (2016).
10. D. Lynch, personal communication (2016).
11. N. J. Pust and J. A. Shaw, "Dual-field imaging polarimeter using liquid crystal variable retarders," *Appl. Opt.* **45**(22), 5470–5478 (2006).
12. N. J. Pust and J. A. Shaw, "Digital all-sky polarization imaging of partly cloudy skies," *Appl. Opt.* **47**(34), H190–H198 (2008).
13. A. R. Dahlberg, N. J. Pust, and J. A. Shaw, "Effects of surface reflectance on skylight polarization measurements at the Mauna Loa Observatory," *Opt. Express* **19**(17), 16008–16021 (2011).
14. N. J. Pust and J. A. Shaw, "Wavelength dependence of the degree of polarization in cloud-free skies: simulations of real environments," *Opt. Express* **20**(14), 15559–15568 (2012).
15. C. F. Bohren, "On the gamut of colors seen through through birefringent airplane windows," *Appl. Opt.* **30**(24), 3474–3478 (1991).
16. C. F. Bohren, "Window watching and polarized light," *Weatherwise* **41**(2), 105–110 (1988).
17. G. E. Shaw, *Fingerprints on the Moon: My Life in Physics*, CreateSpace (2011).
18. G. E. Shaw, "Observations and theoretical reconstruction of the green flash," *Pure Appl. Geophys.* **102**(1), 223–235 (1973).

Chapter 3
Coronas and Iridescence

3.1 Corona

In atmospheric optics, a corona is a set of one or more small colored rings of scattered light surrounding the sun, moon, or other light source. It should not be confused with the sun's outer atmosphere that goes by the same name. As shown in Fig. 2.19, a corona appears near the 0° scattering angle. Observing these colors requires looking close to the sun or moon, so care must be taken to protect your eyes by blocking the direct sun. Coronas are easier to see around the moon ("lunar coronas") because the moon is not such an overwhelmingly bright object.

Corona rings are typically much smaller than halo rings (Fig. 1.1). Laven[1] used Mie scattering simulations to show that the first three red corona rings have angular radii in degrees given by $16/r$, $31/r$, and $47/r$, where r is the radius of the scattering particles in μm. The largest corona rings are formed by the smallest cloud droplets, so typical cloud droplets with a radius of 10 μm would generate corona rings with angular radii of 1.6°, 3.1°, and 4.7°. However, it is quite common to see only the first ring or two. It is a visual treat to see three or more concentric rings.

The conventional explanation says that a corona is formed by light diffracted by spherical water droplets in a cloud. Diffraction causes light incident on a circular object or aperture to spread into a concentric pattern of rings surrounding the light source. Since diffraction is just near-forward scattering, Mie scattering provides a more accurate model of the corona.[1–3] However, insights have been gained using the simple equations for scalar diffraction from a circular obstruction.[4–9] The cloud must be partially transparent so the light passes through the cloud and reaches the observer. All of the droplets must also have a similar size because different particle sizes generate different ring sizes that overlap and smear the colors into a single white ring.

An example of a nice multi-ring corona is shown in Fig. 3.1. I discovered this corona by glancing up while wearing sunglasses as I walked along the Avenue des Champs-Élysées in Paris (sunglasses are great for reducing the glare of forward-scattered light that easily hides a corona). Four distinct red rings were visible by eye and are apparent in the original image. As is commonly done with a convenient object, I used a streetlight to block the direct sunlight in this picture.

Figure 3.1 Corona around the sun (Paris, 5 July 2015).

A lunar corona with a particularly vivid blue ring is shown in Fig. 3.2. The size of the first red ring can be estimated as ~1.3° from the lens focal length and camera sensor size (a quick estimate is also possible by comparing the ring size with the

Figure 3.2 Corona around the moon (Bozeman, MT, 13 Sep. 2014).

0.5° angle occupied by the full moon). This corresponds to a mean cloud particle radius of 12.3 μm based on Laven's relationship mentioned earlier.[1] The much more prominent blue color of this corona compared with the one in Fig. 3.1 is a result of lower cloud optical thickness, probably smaller cloud droplets, and darker nighttime background.[3,5]

An especially large corona appears in Fig. 3.3, which I saw around the sun in a high, thin cloud layer as the airplane I was riding in emerged from a lower, thick cloud layer shortly after takeoff. Laven's relationship[1] indicates that the mean cloud particle radius was only approximately 1.3 μm.

The conditions of an optically thin cloud with small, uniformly sized droplets are often satisfied in wave clouds formed when air is deflected upward by mountains.[4–6] Some years ago a colleague and I realized that many of our wave-cloud corona photographs were taken in meteorological conditions that required the clouds to contain ice crystals, not liquid water droplets. We had always believed that ice crystals were much too large to generate visually discernible diffraction rings. However, a cloud-physics colleague informed us that mountain wave clouds often contain tiny ice particles with effective diameters less than 25 μm. We published our pictures with this hypothesis.[4,5]

Previous measurements had found tiny ice particles in corona-producing cirrus clouds,[7,8] but the first experimental confirmation of ice in corona-generating mountain wave clouds came from the corona in Fig. 3.4. The green laser beam is from one of my laser instruments that we used to determine that the cloud generating these corona rings around the moon was indeed ice.[6] Note that in Fig. 3.4 the circular corona is distorted by my use of a fisheye lens to take this wide-angle photograph (taken at ISO 400 and *f*/2.8 with a 6-s exposure).

Figure 3.3 Corona around the sun in thin clouds (MSP–CDG, 27 May 2016).

Coronas can also be seen around reflections of the sun. Figure 3.5 illustrates examples on a wing and an engine cowling. Figure 3.5(a) shows large corona rings, likely formed when reflected light was scattered by tiny cloud droplets between the wing and my window, whereas Fig. 3.5(b) shows two small sets of corona-like diffraction rings surrounding two reflections of the sun. One reflection is on the cowling, and the other is on a metal band riveted to the cowling. Two overlapping coronas were formed when light from both reflections was diffracted by condensation particles that were collecting on the airplane window. In this case, the light is diffracted by a thin film of tiny water droplets instead of a volume full of droplets, but the optical result is essentially the same as any other corona.

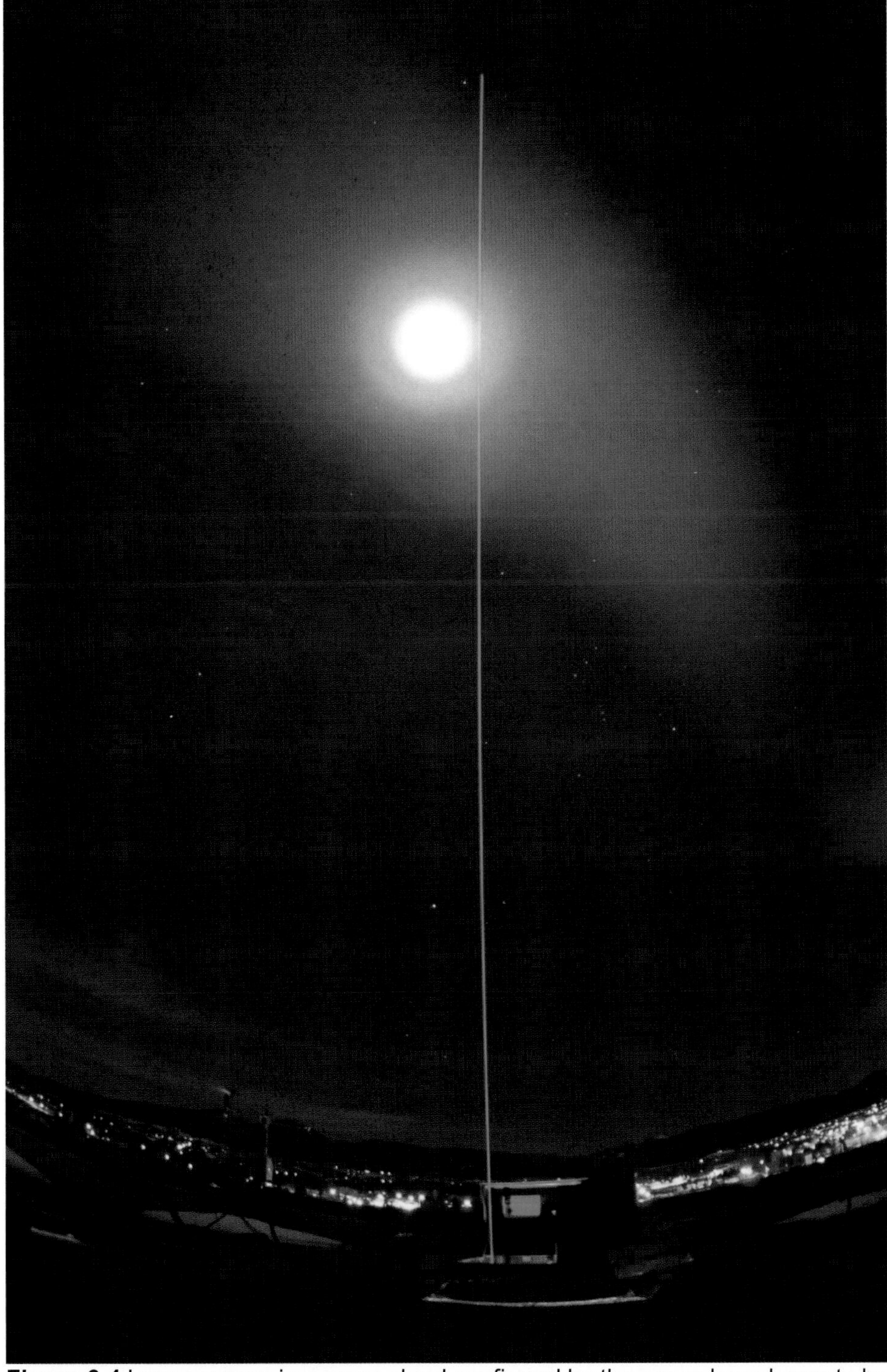

Figure 3.4 Lunar corona in a wave cloud confirmed by the green laser beam to be made of ice particles (Bozeman, MT, 5 Feb. 2009).[6]

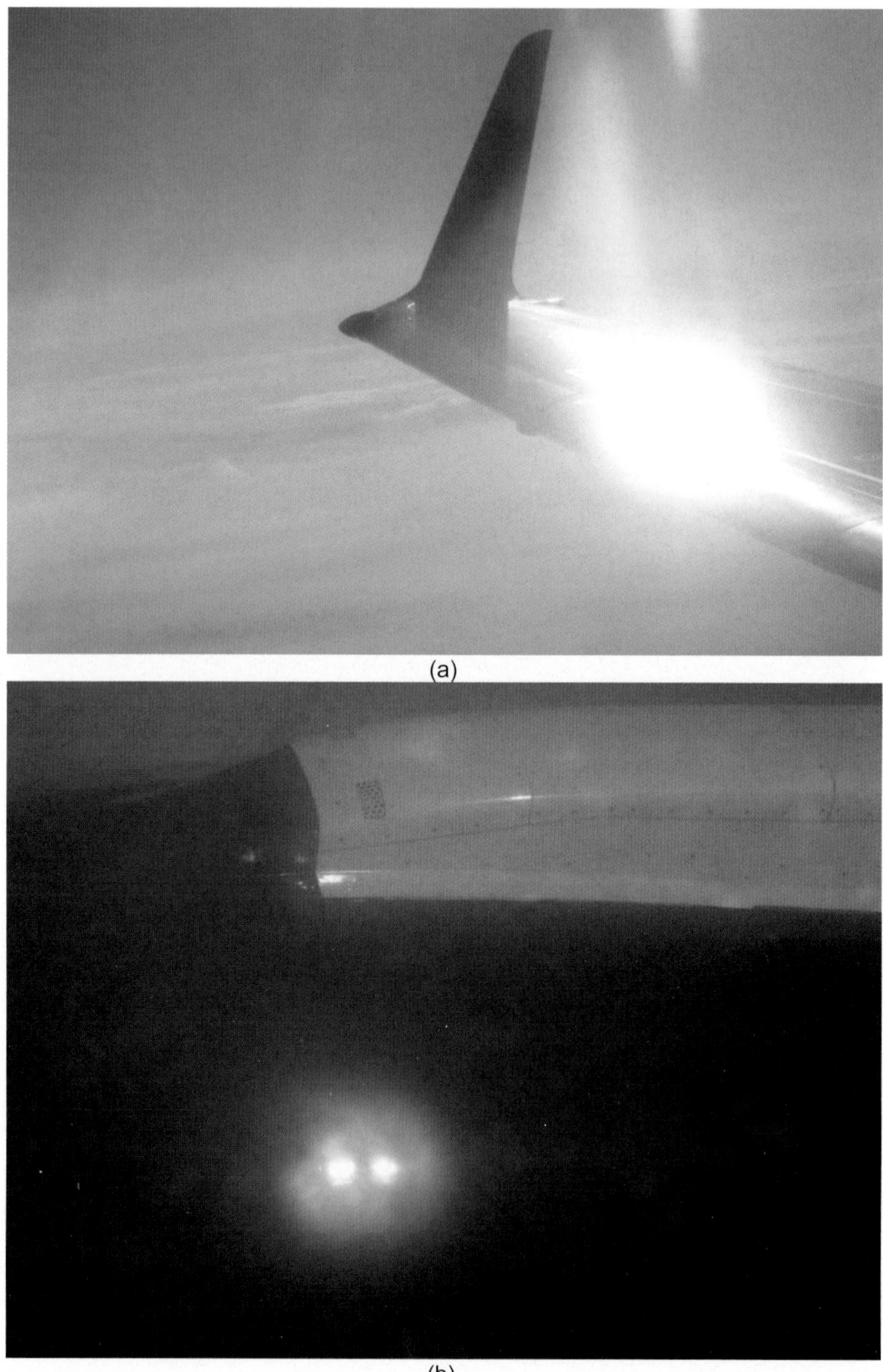

(a)

(b)

Figure 3.5 (a) Corona rings circling the reflection of the sun on an airplane wing (BZN–MSP, 14 Feb. 2012). (b) Dual set of corona rings circling two reflections of the sun on an airplane engine cowling (BZN–MSP, 18 Sep. 2009).

Figure 3.6 shows a set of coronas formed by diffraction of light from reflections of the sun in multiple small lakes in northern Minnesota. Each lake reflection created its own corona, but the multiple coronas are so close together that you have to look closely to realize there is actually a complex pattern of nearby rings. The diffraction occurred when the reflected light encountered small water droplets in the clouds and possibly fog near the ground.

It is quite common to see a corona around the sun or moon from the ground because clouds often exist between us and the sun or moon. However, airplanes spend most of their time flying above all but the highest clouds, which contain ice crystals too large to generate visible diffraction effects. Therefore, the best chances to see a corona from an airplane come while ascending or descending through lower clouds. Years ago I saw an extremely vivid corona from an airplane climbing through low clouds on takeoff from Santa Fe, NM, but it was gone before I could take a photograph. I learned that day how fast things change as an airplane speeds through a cloud! I now point my camera in the proper direction with controls adjusted, ready to hit the shutter button when an optical display briefly appears. Once the plane is through the low clouds, things change more slowly, and I set my camera down (but I always keep it close at hand).

Seeing a corona from the air requires looking through a window on the sunward side of the plane (Fig. 1.1). If you find yourself at a window with severe scratches, you also can look for colors that might arise when the sunlight is diffracted by the tiny scratches, which act like a diffraction grating. Figure 3.7 shows an example of these diffraction colors, which are similar to those that can be observed in spider webs.[10–12]

3.2 Iridescence

As the spatial pattern of particle sizes becomes increasingly random, corona rings turn into a randomized pattern of colors called iridescence. The best colors still require the cloud particles in a small region of the cloud to have a very uniform size distribution. However, the locally uniform sizes vary from one point in the cloud to another. As with the corona, iridescence can be a result of light scattering from small water droplets or tiny ice particles.[6,13] Also like a corona, iridescence involves near-forward scattering, which is usually referred to as diffraction.

A typical display of iridescence is shown in a photograph of a small wispy cloud in Fig. 3.8. A larger and more colorful iridescent cloud is shown in Fig. 3.9. A more dramatic example appears in Fig. 3.10, which is the most colorful display of iridescence I have ever observed (so far). In all these examples the sun was just outside the camera's field of view. I have to laugh a little bit when I remember that I saw the iridescent cloud in Fig. 3.10 after stepping outside my house to take a break from a holiday celebration and family gathering. When I looked into the sky, I was grateful I had needed a social break!

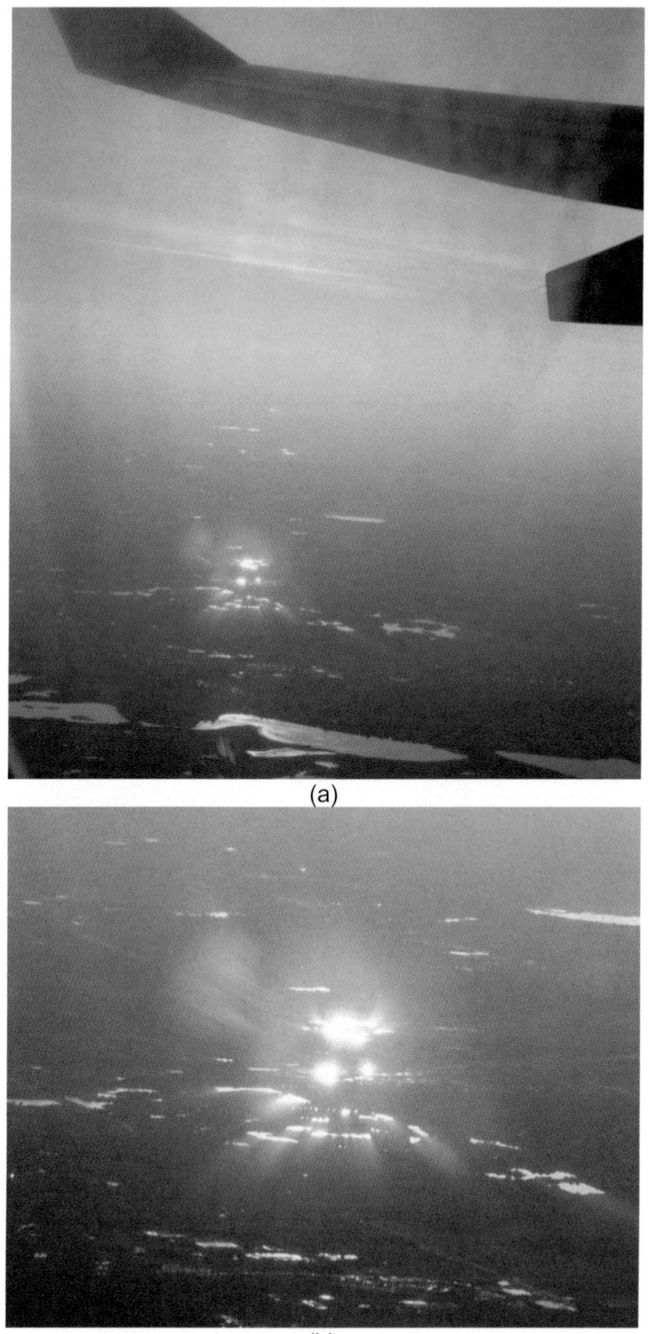

(a)

(b)

Figure 3.6 Corona formed by the diffraction of sunlight reflected from multiple small lakes: (a) wide view to show context and (b) the same image cropped to show details (MSP–AMS, 27 May 2010).

Figure 3.7 Colors from sunlight diffracted by scratches in an airplane window (BZN–SEA, 9 March 2011).

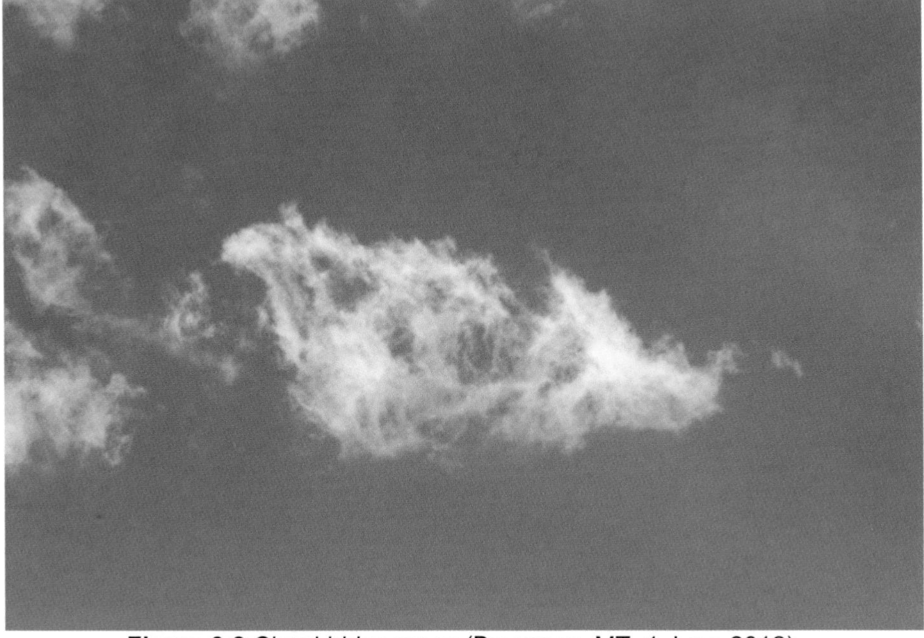

Figure 3.8 Cloud iridescence (Bozeman, MT, 1 June 2012).

Figure 3.9 Cloud iridescence (Bozeman, MT, 26 Nov. 2010).

Figure 3.10 Cloud iridescence (Boulder, CO, Dec. 1999).

Figure 3.11 Iridescence from sunlight diffracted by condensation particles on an airplane window (CTS–HND, 18 March 2016).

I frequently see decent displays of cloud iridescence from airplanes, but one of the more colorful displays (Fig. 3.11) was actually iridescence in condensation on the window. This display, similar to the corona in the bottom photograph of Fig. 3.5, is another example of how condensation that would otherwise be a nuisance can become a key element of a beautiful optical display.

References

1. P. Laven, "Re-visiting the atmospheric corona," *Appl. Opt.* **54**(4), B46–B53 (2015).
2. J. Lock and L. Yang, "Mie theory model of the corona," *Appl. Opt.* **30**, 3408–3414 (1991).
3. S. D. Gedzelman and J. A. Lock, "Simulating coronas in color," *Appl. Opt.* **42**, 497–504 (2003).
4. J. A. Shaw and P. J. Neiman, "Coronas and iridescence in mountain wave clouds," *Appl. Opt.* **42**(3), 476–485 (2003).
5. P. J. Neiman and J. A. Shaw, "Coronas and iridescence in mountain wave clouds over northeastern Colorado," *Bull. Am. Meteorol. Soc.* **84**(10), 1373–1386 (2003).

6. J. A. Shaw and N. J. Pust, "Icy wave-cloud lunar corona and cirrus iridescence," *Appl. Opt.* **50**, F6–F11 (2011).
7. K. Sassen, "Corona-producing cirrus cloud properties derived from polarization lidar and photographic analyses," *Appl. Opt.* **30**, 3421–3428 (1991).
8. K. Sassen, G. G. Mace, J. Hallett, and M. R. Poellot, "Corona-producing ice clouds: A case study of a cold mid-latitude cirrus layer," *Appl. Opt.* **37**, 1477–1485 (1998).
9. L. Cowley, P. Laven, and M. Vollmer, "Rings around the sun and moon: coronae and diffraction," *Eur. J. Phys.* **40**(1), 51–59 (2005).
10. R. G. Greenler and J. W. Hable, "Colors in spider webs," *Am. Sci.* **77**(4), 369–373 (1989).
11. W. Livingston, "Glorious visions: colour and light in nature," *J. Br. Astron. Assoc.* **115**(5), 247–249 (2005).
12. W. Suhr and H. J. Schlichting, "On the colours of spider web-orbs," *Eur. J. Phys.* **32**(2), 615–624 (2011).
13. K. Sassen, "Iridescence in an aircraft contrail," *J. Opt. Soc. Amer.* **69**, 1080–1084 (1979).

Chapter 4
Rainbows and Cloudbows

4.1 Rainbow Colors and Geometry

Not all colored arcs or rings are rainbows, but rainbows might be the most recognizable. There is something visually irresistible about the transformation of everyday sunlight into previously hidden colors. One of my hopes with this book is that more people will begin to recognize the existence and uniqueness of other colored arcs—coronas, glories, halos—as well as rainbows. However, this chapter is all about the beautiful phenomenon we call the rainbow.

As its name implies, a rainbow is a bow in the sky that is formed when light interacts with raindrops. Actually, water drops from any source will suffice, whether rain, a garden hose, or a fountain. Figure 4.1 illustrates the bright colors a rainbow can produce under the right conditions. Figure 4.2 reminds us of the beauty and impressive size of a double rainbow, and Fig. 4.3 gives a closer look at a double rainbow to emphasize the reversal of colors between the primary and secondary bows. Notice also how dark the sky is between the bows, a region called Alexander's dark band (an angular region from where light is effectively removed to create the rainbow).

Much of what we see in a rainbow can be explained with geometric optical ray tracing, although the details require more complicated theories.[1–6] The basic explanation relies on refraction (bending) and reflection of light inside rain drops. The simple explanation relies on fictionally spherical drops; real ones (especially large drops) are shaped more like pillows than spheres but never like the tear drop so widely used to denote rain in popular media.[7–10] Nevertheless, valuable insight can be gained with a simple, spherical rain-drop model.

Rainbows are colored because light entering and leaving a rain drop refracts, or bends, by an amount that depends on the wavelength. This is called dispersion—the same mechanism that produces colors from a prism. For water, glass, and many optical materials, blue light refracts more strongly than red light. As a convenient pair, we often discuss blue and red light with the understanding that a continuous spectrum of colors actually exists within white light. However, the color purity in rainbows is reduced well below 100% by competing background light and other factors,[11–14] although the rainbow still presents the purest colors of all atmospheric optical phenomena other than a reddened sun.[11]

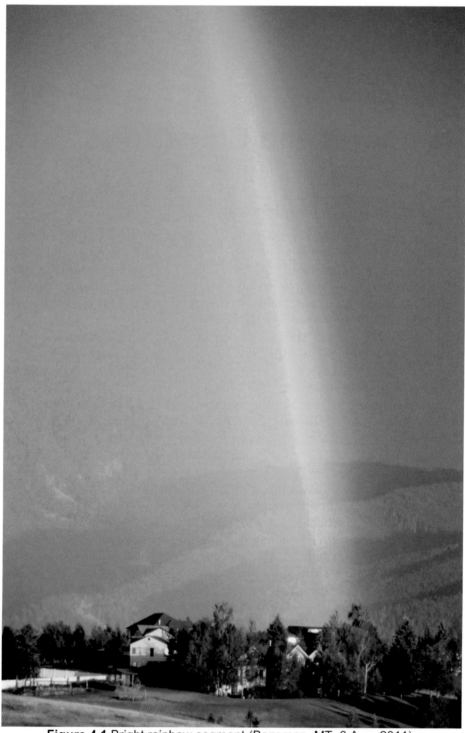

Figure 4.1 Bright rainbow segment (Bozeman, MT, 6 Aug. 2011).

Figure 4.2 Double rainbow centered on the shadow of my head at the anti-solar point (Bozeman, MT, 9 Aug. 2010).

Figure 4.3 Close-up view of a double rainbow (Bozeman, MT, 6 Aug. 2011).

Figure 4.4 "Just add water to see the keychain." Light bending in water allows us to see a keychain that is hidden behind the front of the pot.

Refraction is the bending of light at an interface between materials of differing density, such as water and air. It explains why your legs seem to bend in a funny way when you stand in knee-deep water. It also explains why those who rely on spear fishing to provide fish for dinner learn to aim low. This is illustrated by the two photographs in Fig. 4.4. The key chain sitting at the bottom of a metal container was not visible in the empty pot (left) but became visible when the pot was filled with water (right). Nothing else changed—the key chain simply became visible because the light rays coming from the keychain were bent toward the camera at the water–air interface.

Figure 4.5 shows example ray paths for blue and red light through a spherical water drop. The sketches are for the primary rainbow on the left and the secondary rainbow on the right. White light from the sun bends at the air–water interface by an amount that depends on the color. For the primary bow, some of the color-separated light reflects from the back of the drop, and the colors become further dispersed by a second refraction as the light exits the water–air interface.

Although not shown explicitly in Fig. 4.5, keep in mind that much of the light passes through the back of the rain drop. Otherwise, rainbows would be blindingly bright (a small amount of light also reflects from the air–water interface refraction points). Also not shown explicitly is that a bundle of parallel rays that strike the drop at different points all bend differently and exit the drop at different angles. However, there is a concentration of rays near the angle where the light is bent by the smallest amount. This angle, called the angle of minimum deviation,[15] is where we see most of the rainbow light. It will arise again in our discussion of halos created by refraction in ice crystals.

The ray paths for the secondary rainbow include two reflections from the back of the water drop. Because an additional large amount of light is transmitted out of the drop at the second reflection point, the secondary bow is much less bright than the primary bow (Figs. 4.2 and 4.3). The added reflection also causes a reversal of colors between the primary and secondary bow, as shown in Fig. 4.3.

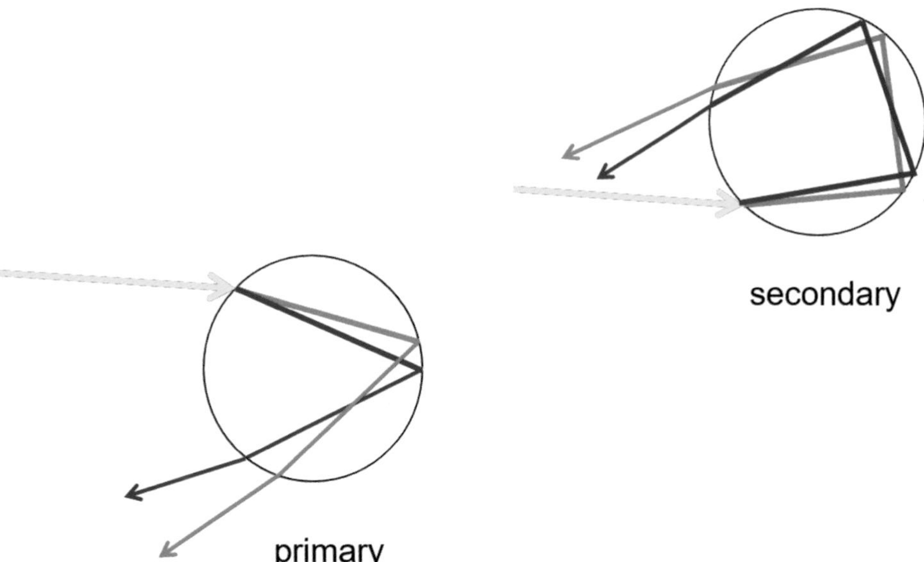

Figure 4.5 Sketch of ray paths through a spherical water droplet with one internal reflection for the primary bow and two reflections for the secondary bow.

Notice that the color order is determined by the angle from which the light appears to come when it reaches your eye, not which ray is on top or bottom as they emerge from the drop. In fact, simultaneously seeing more than one brilliant color requires more than a single drop. Figure 4.6 indicates that the different colors you see in a rainbow come from a multitude of drops. If you look near the rainbow angle at a single drop of water clinging to a flower petal, for example, you will have to move your head slightly up or down to see different colors. This is also a great way to make your neighbors wonder what you are doing so that you can strike up a conversation about rainbows!

There are even higher-order rainbows, but so far they have only been seen in digitally processed images. Their brightness is too weak to be seen easily by the eye, especially given that the third- and fourth-order bows lie back toward the bright sun. Nevertheless, an insightful analysis[16] recently motivated careful observers to discover 3rd-, 4th-, 5th-, and 7th-order rainbows in digital images.[17–20]

To see a conventional primary and secondary rainbow, look away from the sun because the rainbow rings are circles centered on the anti-solar point. They are very large circles, as you can see from the angles shown in Figs. 4.6 and 4.7. However, we see only the portion of the circle that lies above our horizon in the vicinity of sun-illuminated rain drops. The double rainbow in Fig. 4.8 was sitting low on the horizon because it was formed early in the afternoon when the sun was still high in the sky. As the sun sets, the rainbow rises with the anti-solar point on the opposite horizon. Consequently, the primary rainbow cannot be seen above a flat horizon unless the sun elevation angle is less than about 42° (unless the water drops are nearby, as in the case of a rainbow formed in a fountain[21]).

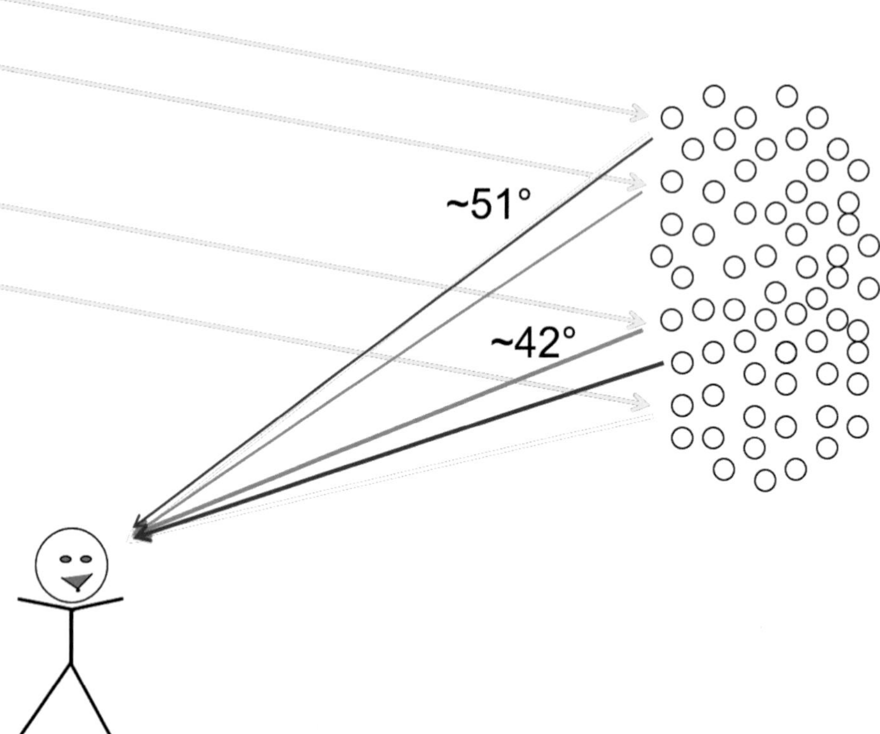

Figure 4.6 Nominal observing angles for primary and secondary rainbows.

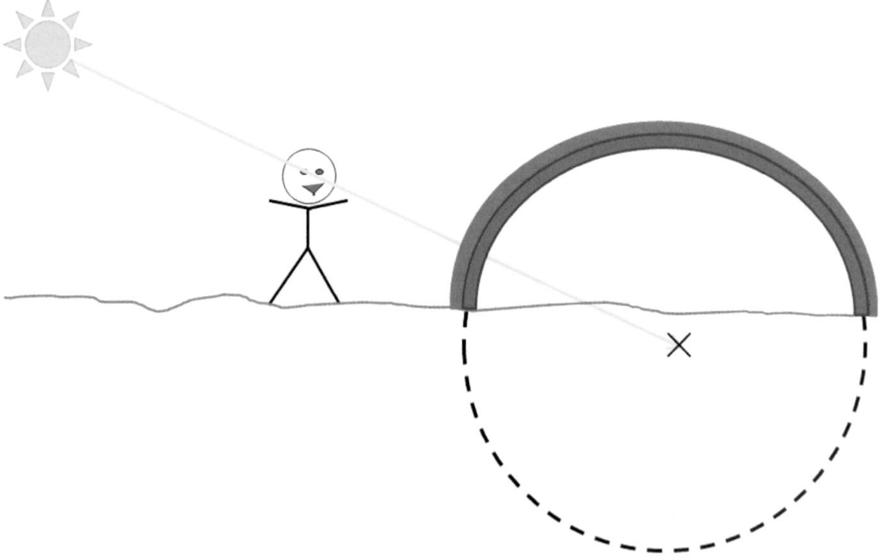

Figure 4.7 A rainbow is a large circle centered on the anti-solar point but is only visible in the portion of the circle located above the horizon amidst illuminated raindrops.

Figure 4.8 Double rainbow rising from the horizon opposite the setting sun (Paradise Valley, MT, 13 July 2010).

Both primary and secondary bows are formed by rays clustered near the minimum deviation angle.[15] The less concentrated light rays at larger deviation angles contribute to the brightness seen inside the primary bow for ray paths with one internal reflection. Similarly, rays exceeding the minimum deviation angle for paths with two reflections contribute to the brightness seen outside the secondary bow. The resulting lack of light between the primary and secondary bow creates Alexander's dark band (Figs. 4.1, 4.2, 4.3, and 4.8).

From the air, a mountaintop, or any elevated location, it is possible to see more than a hemispheric rainbow because there is no surface to block our view below the horizon. Nevertheless, because raindrops often fall in a limited volume of air, you will most often see fairly normal-sized rainbows from an airplane. Like rainbows observed from the ground, their colors can be captivating, as was the case with the pretty double rainbow segment in Fig. 4.9, which appeared on descent into Fairbanks, Alaska.

The photograph in Fig. 4.10 provides a clue that rainbows seen from the air can extend well below the horizon. This one was really fun to see because it was formed in rain drops blown upward by the wind, and it existed in a mostly cloud-free region of the sky just outside my window on a flight leaving Honolulu, HI. Only a portion of the rainbow is visible, though, because the rain drops filled only a small region of the sky.

The photographs in Figs. 4.11 and 4.12 show remarkably beautiful full-circle rainbows that can be seen from the air if sunlight illuminates rain drops that fill a huge portion of the sky. I carry a fisheye lens with me on all flights, partly so I am prepared when one of my flights encounters a situation like this. You can see that even the wide-angle lens used for Fig. 4.11 was not wide enough to capture the full 102° secondary bow. The lens used for the mountaintop rainbow in Fig. 4.12 was wide enough, but the secondary bow was quite faint.

Figure 4.9 Double rainbow seen on descent into Fairbanks, AK (BRW–FAI, 14 July 2012).

Figure 4.10 Rainbow extending below the horizon (HNL–ITO, 16 July 2000).

Figure 4.11 Full-circle rainbow seen from a drone (near Greenville, SC, 15 Jan. 2016). Image printed with permission from Brad Hudson.

4.2 Cloudbows and Fogbows

When rain drops are replaced by much smaller cloud or fog droplets, diffraction broadens the bow and smears the colors into a white cloudbow or fogbow.[1,22–24] Rain drop radii are typically near 1 mm, whereas cloud and fog droplets are generally smaller than 0.1 mm (100 μm), often near 10 μm. A cloudbow is quite often visible on the clouds below an airplane, and, as with a conventional rainbow, a cloud or fogbow is circular and centered on the anti-solar point (Fig. 4.13).

To find a cloudbow, look for a streak of cloud that is brighter than its surroundings in an arc lying about 42° in any direction from the anti-solar point. You may see one extending above what you would normally consider the top of the cloud (Fig. 4.14), but most cloudbows will appear spread across the clouds below you (Fig. 4.15).

Figure 4.12 Full-circle red rainbow seen from a mountaintop observatory (Mt. Zugspitze, Germany, 8 July 2014). Image reprinted with permission from Claudia Hinz.

Figure 4.13 Full-circle fogbow photographed with a 15-mm fisheye lens from the ship National Geographic Explorer (King Oscar Fjord, Eastern Greenland). Image reprinted with permission from Ralph Lee Hopkins.

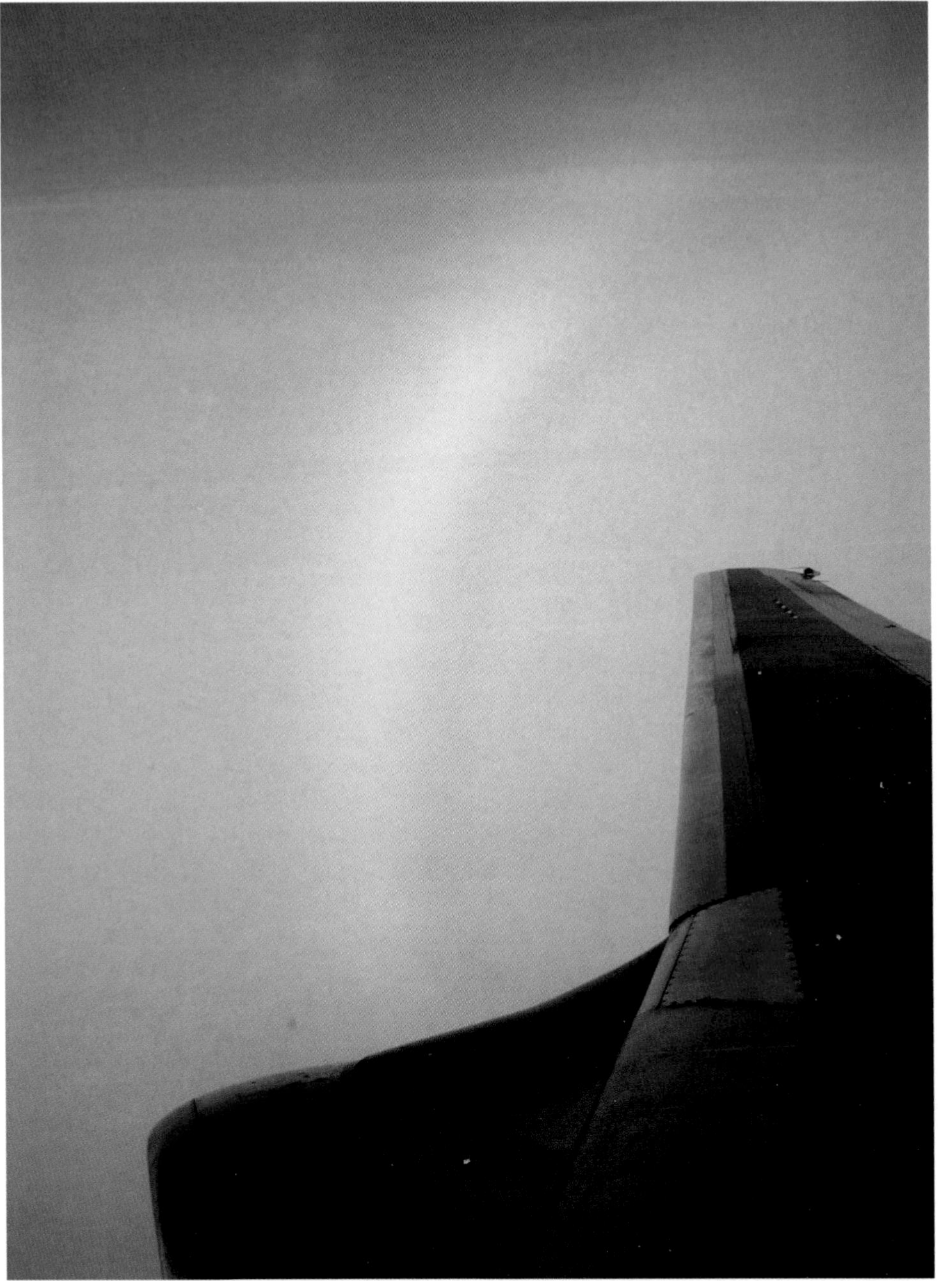

Figure 4.14 Cloudbow that extends into droplets in the air, located above what would normally be considered the top of the cloud (FAI–BRW, 6 April 2004).

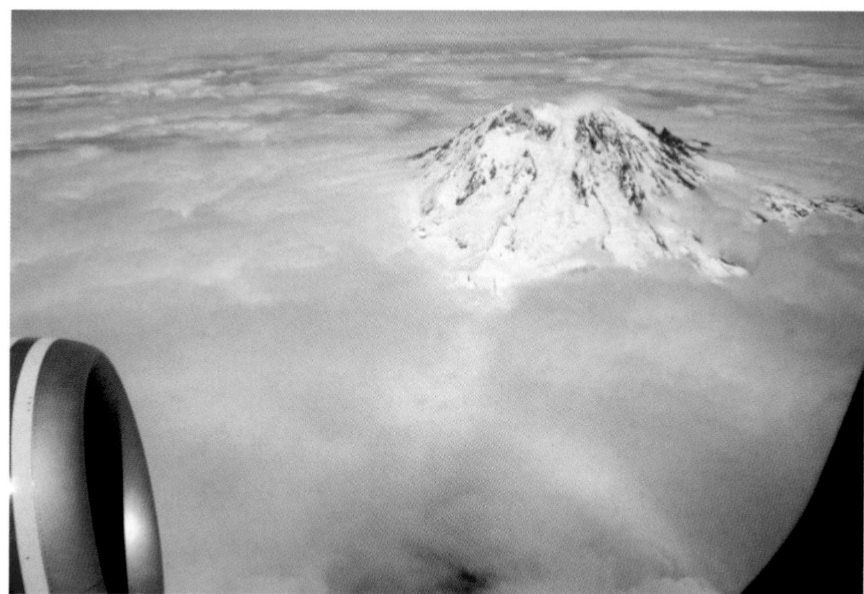

Figure 4.15 Cloudbow (SEA–SLC, 21 June 2013).

You can even see cloudbows or rainbows at night if you look carefully near the time of a full moon. Observation from an airplane requires shielding the window from reflections of interior light, as I did for the lunar cloudbow photograph in Fig. 4.16. Just to make sure this was what I thought it was, I took another picture from an unoccupied seat on the other side of the plane. That picture is not shown here, but it confirmed that the moon was in exactly the correct position to create this lunar cloudbow (off the left side and about 45° forward). The brightening sky on the right edge of Fig. 4.16 is where the sun was beginning to rise during this early morning flight.

4.3 Rainbow and Cloudbow Polarization

You can increase the contrast between a rainbow or cloudbow and the background with polarizing sunglasses or a polarizing filter on your camera. Alternatively, if you somehow do not like rainbows, you can make them disappear with the same tools, but you can only make pieces of the bow disappear, not the whole thing at once. The light from the rainbow is strongly polarized because the reflection at the back of the drop is near the Brewster angle, where reflected light is 100% polarized.

There are two competing processes for rainbow polarization, and they each favor orthogonal polarization directions. The refractions produce weak polarization radial to the bow, whereas the reflection produces strong polarization tangential to the bow. The net effect is that the light from the primary bow is more than 90% polarized tangential to the bow (nearly vertically polarized at the sides of a rainbow, like Fig. 4.17, and horizontally polarized at the top of a rainbow, like

Figure 4.16 Lunar cloudbow photographed on the first leg of a trip to Sapporo, Japan (BZN–SEA, 27 Jan. 2016).

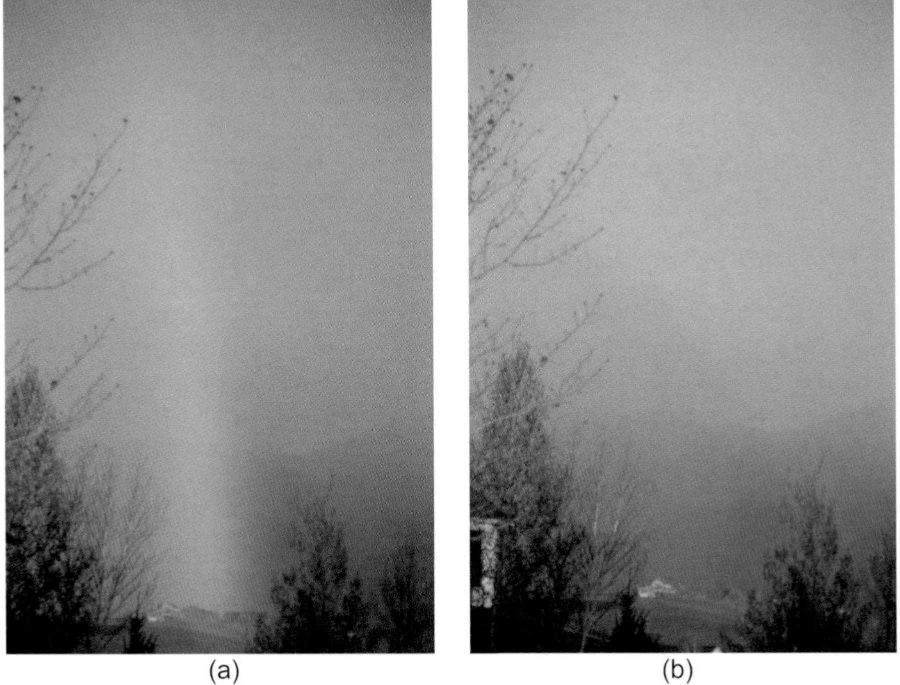

(a) (b)

Figure 4.17 Rainbow polarization illustrated with a (a) nearly vertical polarizer and (b) nearly horizontal polarizer (Bozeman, MT, 20 May 2010).

Fig. 4.2).[25–29] Figure 4.17(a) was taken with a near-vertical polarizer to enhance the lower end of this late-afternoon rainbow, whereas Fig. 4.17(b) was taken with a nearly horizontal polarizer to suppress the rainbow. A secondary bow is only about 50% polarized, and a cloudbow is also less polarized than a primary rainbow. Nevertheless, a polarizing filter can enhance the visibility of a cloudbow, but doing this from an airplane also generates additional colors from the birefringent window, as is seen in Fig. 4.18 (these colors are discussed further in Sections 1.2.3 and 10.2).

4.4 Supernumerary Bows

Sometimes we see what appear to be extra colored bands on the inside of a rainbow, as can be seen in Fig. 4.19 and Fig. 4.20. Their name, supernumerary bows, means just that: extra bows. They are not predicted by the ray-tracing explanation presented earlier but instead require a wave-optics approach. As was shown in Fig. 2.19, rainbows and cloudbows, as well as supernumerary bands, are all predicted by Mie scattering calculations. In recent years the wider availability of Mie scattering codes has led to many insights into the visual nature of rainbows and cloudbows.[1–6,16,23,24]

Supernumerary bands arise from interference (or superposition) of light that passes through a raindrop along slightly different paths. They occur most prominently for small drops with a radius near 0.25 mm,[30] and the number of visible bands is severely limited by the low coherence of sunlight.[31] Real raindrops are flattened oblate spheroids that fall with their long axis oriented horizontally,[7–10] so the most visible interference fringes arise from light passing through the narrower vertical axis. Therefore, we see supernumerary bands most often along the top of a rainbow. For cloudbows, which do not involve falling raindrops, the most visually apparent supernumerary bands result from the smallest spherical cloud droplets.[23,24]

4.5 Red and Infrared Rainbows

We have seen that scattering in a long path removes all of the colors from sunlight except the long-wavelength oranges and reds. Therefore, when the sun is low on the horizon, we can see a red rainbow (Fig. 4.21). We can capture even longer wavelengths by using a filter on the camera that blocks visible light and transmits near-infrared light. Because the camera sensor responds to this light, it can record a photograph of the otherwise invisible infrared rainbow (Fig. 4.22).[32,33] This infrared rainbow photograph was recorded with a standard digital single-lens-reflex (DSLR) camera in near-infrared light with wavelengths beyond 700 nm. By carefully comparing the two photographs in Fig. 4.22, you can see that the infrared rainbow lies just outside the visible rainbow. Notice also how bright the tree leaves are at these infrared wavelengths.[32]

Figure 4.18 Polarization-enhanced white cloudbow (ANC–SEA, 14 Jan. 2016). Note the colors caused by the birefringent window (see Section 10.2).

Figure 4.19 Supernumerary bands on the inside of a rainbow (Bozeman, MT, 10 July 2016).

Figure 4.20 Supernumerary band on the inside of a cloudbow (BZN–MSP, 20 Aug. 2007).

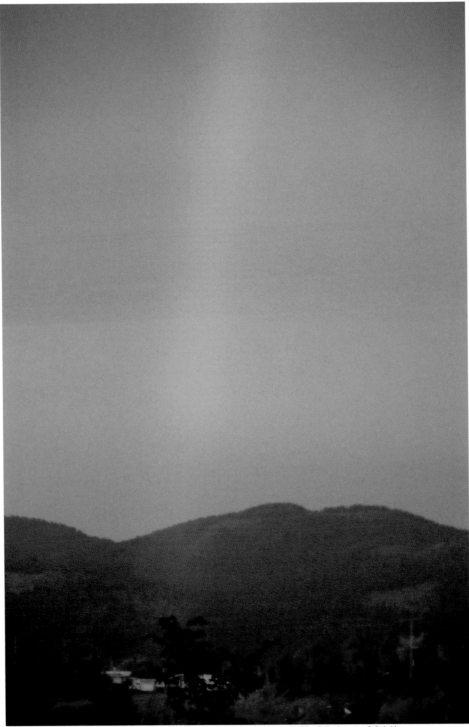

Figure 4.21 Red rainbow (Bozeman, MT, 25 June 2011).

(a)

(b)

Figure 4.22 (a) Near-infrared rainbow corresponding to the (b) visible rainbow (Bozeman, MT, 25 June 2011).

References

1. D. K. Lynch and P. Schwartz, "Rainbows and fogbows," *Appl. Opt.* **30**(24), 3415–3420 (1991).
2. S. D. Gedzelman, "Simulating rainbows and halos in color," *Appl. Opt.* **33**(21), 4607–4613 (1994).
3. R. L. Lee, Jr., "Mie theory, Airy theory, and the natural rainbow," *Appl. Opt.* **37**(9), 1506–1519 (1998).
4. J. A. Adam, "The mathematical physics of rainbows and glories," *Phys. Reports* **356**(4), 229–365 (2002).
5. P. Laven, "Simulation of rainbows, coronas, and glories, by use of Mie theory," *Appl. Opt.* **42**(3), 436–444 (2003).
6. S. D. Gedzelman, "Simulating rainbows in their natural environment," *Appl. Opt.* **47**(34), H176–H181 (2008).
7. J. E. McDonald, "The shape of raindrops," *Sci. Am.* **190**(2), 64–68 (1954).
8. H. R. Pruppacher and K. V. Beard, "A wind tunnel investigation of the internal circulation and shape of water drops falling at terminal velocity in air," *Quar. J. Royal Meteorol. Soc.* **96**(408), 247–256 (1970).
9. K. V. Beard, V. N. Bringi, and M. Thurai, "A new understanding of raindrop shape," *J. Atmos. Sci.* **97**(4), 396–415 (2010).
10. A. B. Fraser, "Inhomogeneities in the Color and Intensity of the Rainbow," *J. Atmos. Sci.* **29**, 211–212 (1972).
11. R. L. Lee, Jr., "What are 'all the colors of the rainbow'?" *Appl. Opt.* **30**(24), 3401–3407 (1991).
12. S. D. Gedzelman, "Visibility of Halos and Rainbows," *Appl. Opt.* **19**, 3068–3074 (1980).
13. S. D. Gedzelman, "Rainbow Brightness," *Appl. Opt.* **21**, 3032–3037 (1982).
14. J. N. Kidder, "Colors of the spectrum: Do you wonder where the yellow went?" *Appl. Opt.* **33**(21), 4727–4732 (1994).
15. J. D. Walker, "Multiple rainbows from single drops of water and other liquids," *Am. J. Phys.* **44**(5), 421–433 (1976).
16. R. L. Lee, Jr. and P. Laven, "Visibility of natural tertiary rainbows," *Appl. Opt.* **50**(28), F152–F161 (2011).
17. M. Großmann, E. Schmidt, and A. Haußmann, "Photographic evidence for the third-order rainbow," *Appl. Opt.* **50**(28), F134–F141 (2011).
18. M. Theusner, "Photographic observation of a natural fourth-order rainbow," *Appl. Opt.* **50**(28), F129–F133 (2011).
19. H. E. Edens, "Photographic observation of a natural fifth-order rainbow," *Appl. Opt.* **54**(4), B26–B29 (2015).

20. H. E. Edens and G. P. Können, "Probable photographic detection of the natural seventh-order rainbow," *Appl. Opt.* **54**(4), B93–B96 (2015).
21. S. D. Gedzelman and J. Hernández-Andrés, "Fountain rainbows," *Appl. Opt.* **47**(34), H220–H224 (2008).
22. D. K. Lynch and S. N. Futterman, "Uloa's observation of the glory, fogbow, and an unidentified phenomenon," *Appl. Opt.* **30**(24), 3538–3541 (1991).
23. S. D. Gedzelman, "Simulating glories and cloudbows in color," *Appl. Opt.* **42**(3), 429–435 (2003).
24. http://www.atoptics.co.uk/droplets/fogdrpsz.htm
25. G. P. Können and J. H. de Boer, "Polarized rainbow," *Appl. Opt.* **18**(12), 1961–1965 (1979).
26. G. P. Können, *Polarized Light in Nature*, Cambridge University Press, Cambridge (1985).
27. A. Barta, G. Horvath, B. Bernáth, and V. B. Meyer-Rochow, "Imaging polarimetry of the rainbow," *Appl. Opt.* **42**(3), 399–405 (2003).
28. G. Horvath, R. Hededűs, A. Barta, A. Farkas, and S. Åkesson, "Imaging polarimetry of the fogbow: polarization characteristics of white rainbows measured in the high Arctic," *Appl. Opt.* **50**(28), F64–F71 (2011).
29. G. P. Können, "Polarization and visibility of higher-order rainbows," *Appl. Opt.* **54**(4), B35–B40 (2015).
30. A. B. Fraser, "Why can the supernumerary bows be seen in a rain shower?" *J. Opt. Soc. Am.* **73**(12), 1626–1628 (1983).
31. J. A. Lock, "Observability of Atmospheric Glories and Supernumerary Rainbows," *J. Opt. Soc. Am. A* **6**, 1924–1930 (1989).
32. K. Mangold, J. A. Shaw, and M. Vollmer, "The physics of near infrared photography," *Eur. J. Phys.* **34**(6), S51 (2013).
33. R. G. Greenler, "Infrared rainbow," *Science* **173**(4003), 1231–1232 (1971).

Chapter 5
Glories

5.1 Glory Geometry

A glory is one of the optical phenomena best observed from an airplane. It is a small set of colored circles centered on the anti-solar point, in the direction directly opposite the sun. To find where the glory should be, imagine a line reaching from the sun, through your head, and extending onward to infinity. During the day, the anti-solar point lies below the horizon by the same angle that the sun is above the horizon. This is also the location of the airplane's shadow, so the glory is actually a small circle of light in the airplane's shadow.

Figure 5.1 shows a glory formed by sunlight scattering in the near-backward direction from the water droplets in the cloud below my airplane. We had just passed through the cloud on our ascent out of Seattle and were close enough that the airplane's shadow was still visible on the cloud.

Figure 5.1 Glory on clouds during an ascent out of Seattle (SEA–BZN, 3 Oct. 2015).

A glory has similarities to a corona and has on occasion been referred to as an anti-corona,[1] a meaningful description since the glory exists in exactly the opposite region of the sky compared with the corona. Like the corona, a glory can have one or more rings, depending on the size and uniformity of the cloud droplets. Figure 5.2 shows two photographs of glories with multiple colored rings. Figure 5.3 shows a multi-ring glory with a cloudbow to its left. Both the glory and the cloudbow are circles centered on the anti-solar point, so you can also think of the glory as a small circle sitting at the center of the much larger circle of the cloudbow. To see both at once requires a cloud with uniform water droplets extending over a large angular region that is visible from your airplane window and not obscured by an engine or wing.

Also like the corona, the size of the glory rings is inversely proportional to the size of the scattering droplets, although the same droplets give rise to different sized glories and coronas. The largest glories arise from the smallest water droplets, and achieving distinct colors requires a very uniform cloud-droplet-size distribution.

Unlike a corona, simple diffraction theory cannot be used to quickly calculate the size or colors of glory rings; instead, a full scattering theory is required.[2] Previous studies showed that a glory arises largely from the last few significant terms in the Mie scattering calculation, and these terms can be physically related to optical rays that graze the surface of the scattering object (Mie scattering is computed as a series of mathematical terms).[3] In recent years Mie scattering calculations have been used to model glories in realistic environments and in full color.[4–6] Laven used this approach to determine that the angular radius in degrees is given for the first four red glory rings by $24/r$, $37/r$, $56/r$, and $75/r$, where r is the radius of the scattering droplet.[6]

The best glories result from scattering by cloud droplets with a radius of 10 μm or smaller, and the best cloudbows result from scattering by droplets with a radius of 10 μm or larger.[4] A cloudbow becomes a white band with a droplet radius near 6 μm and begins to exhibit a slightly colored inner edge and hints of supernumerary bands when the droplet radius is greater than approximately 10 μm. A cloudbow would begin to look like a rainbow with a droplet radius greater than approximately 50 μm, but such large droplets can hardly exist at the top of a cloud. Glories and cloudbows are generally most visually appealing when observed in fairly thin clouds from a position near the cloud and with a dark background.[4] Therefore, you should pay closest attention in your search for glories when the airplane is just emerging from or just entering a cloud layer.

Sometimes when the airplane is close to a cloud, the airplane's contrail (exhaust plume) casts a visible shadow (see Section 6.3). The contrail shadow can help lead your eyes to the glory, as in Fig. 5.4.

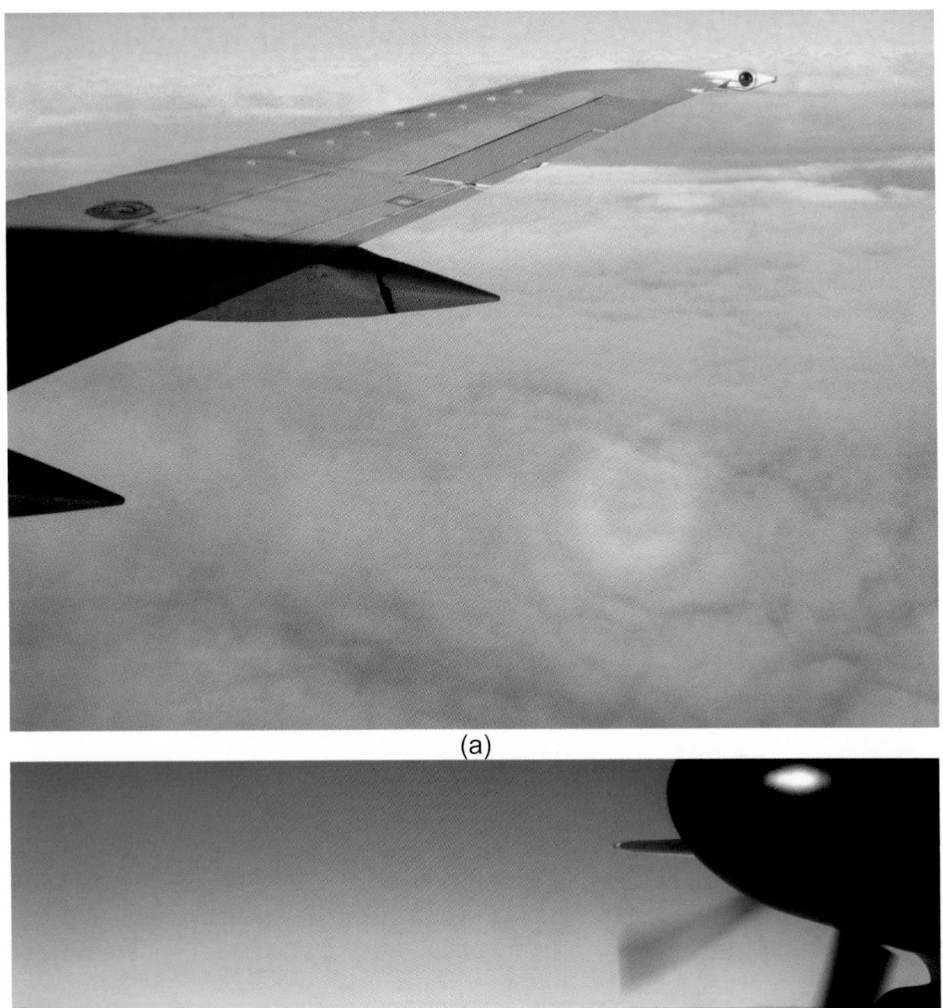

(a)

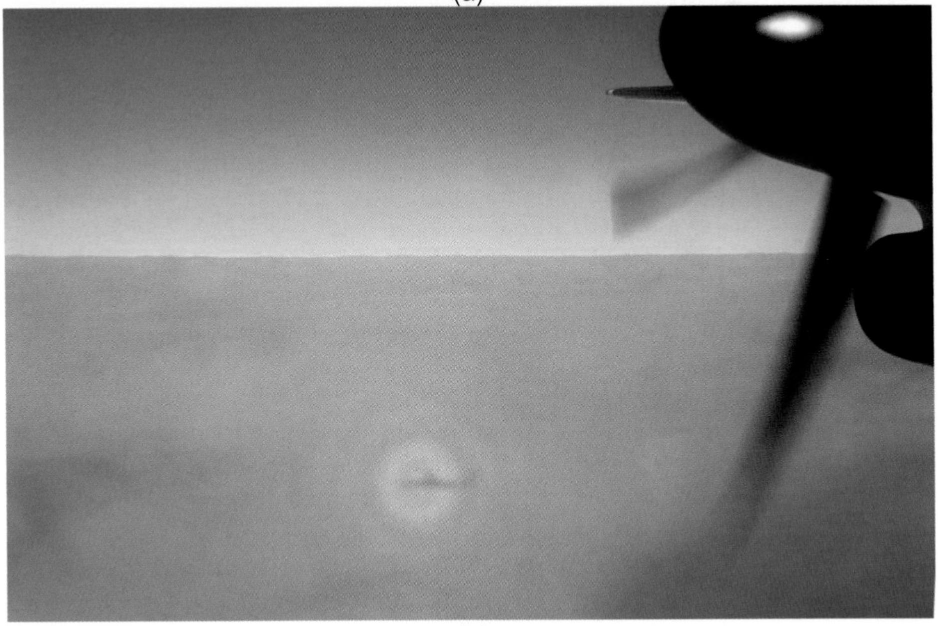

(b)

Figure 5.2 Glories with multiple rings: (a) FAI–ANC, 10 April. 2004 and (b) BZN–SEA, 8 Jan. 2016.

Figure 5.3 The glory is located at the anti-solar point, which is also at the center of the cloudbow (FAI–BRW, 1 Aug. 2013).

5.2 Glories and Airplane Shadows

We have already noted that the center of a glory is located at the anti-solar point, which is also the center of a cloudbow. But even more specifically, the center of a glory is at the location of the shadow of the observer's head. Therefore, when you can see details of the airplane shadow in a photograph of a glory, you can immediately determine where in the airplane the photographer was seated. For example, both Figs. 5.1 and 5.2(b) show clearly that I was seated just forward of the wing on those flights. If you look very closely at Fig. 5.3, you may just resolve a tiny airplane shadow that suggests that I was sitting just forward of the wing on that flight as well, although in this case you can see the wing in the picture, so no glory-and-shadow sleuthing is needed. However, there is not a sufficiently discernible airplane shadow in Fig. 5.2(a) to indicate my location on that flight.

At this point you might be asking yourself why the airplane shadow is so obvious in two of the photographs shown so far in this chapter yet so absent in the other two. The explanation lies in the difference between the size of a glory and the size of a shadow. A glory (like a corona, cloudbow, or rainbow) is an angular scattering phenomenon in which light is redirected into a specific range of angles. As the observer gets further away from the cloud, the glory remains the same angular size (but its brightness eventually fades into the background as the glory light is spread over a larger and larger area). A shadow, on the other hand, occupies an angle that becomes steadily smaller with increasing distance, so at some distance it becomes too small to be seen by the eye.

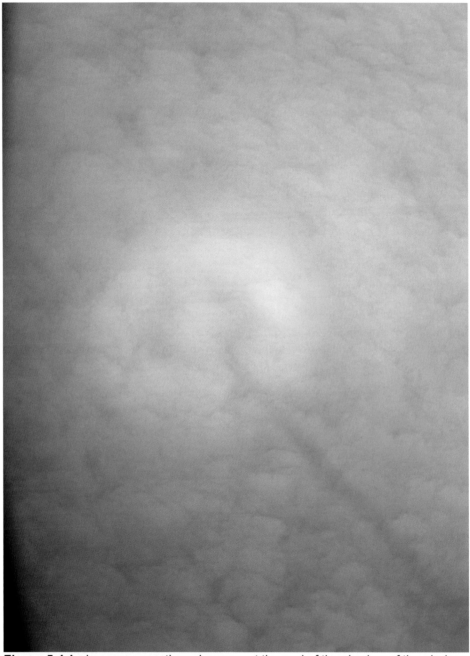

Figure 5.4 A glory can sometimes be seen at the end of the shadow of the airplane contrail (SEA–ANC, 13 March 2005).

Up close, a shadow has the same size as the airplane. However, at greater distances the shadow becomes smaller because the angular width of the sun causes light rays to arrive at the airplane with a 0.5° angular spread (this behavior is discussed further in Section 6.1). Ignoring this angular spreading for the moment, at a distance of 200 m a 20-m-long airplane would cast a shadow enclosing an angle of 20/200 = 0.1 radian (100 mrad, or 5.7°). In this case, the shadow and glory would have similar sizes. However, at a typical flight altitude of 10,000 m, the 20-m shadow would occupy only 20/10,000 = 0.002 radian (2 mrad, or 0.11°), which is many times smaller than the glory. Including the 0.5° angular width of the sun makes things even worse. In this case, the distinct shadow of the airplane with width d would be washed out by light from the sun edge at a distance of approximately $d/\tan(0.5°)$. Thus, the distinct shadow of the 20-m airplane would disappear at a distance of only 2.3 km.

This calculation tells us that glories observed on nearby clouds can be accompanied by airplane shadows as large as, or even larger than, the glory, but beyond several hundred meters the glory will appear without a discernible airplane shadow. Figure 5.5 shows a distinct airplane shadow and glory on a cloud. Can you determine the location of my seat based on the geometry of the scene?

The four images in Figs. 5.6 and 5.7 show an airplane shadow that grew larger as the airplane descended closer to and then into the clouds, whereas the glory maintained a constant angular size. In Fig. 5.7(b), the airplane was in the top of the cloud, so the airplane shadow was much larger than the glory and was distorted by the rapid changes in the nearby clouds and available illumination.

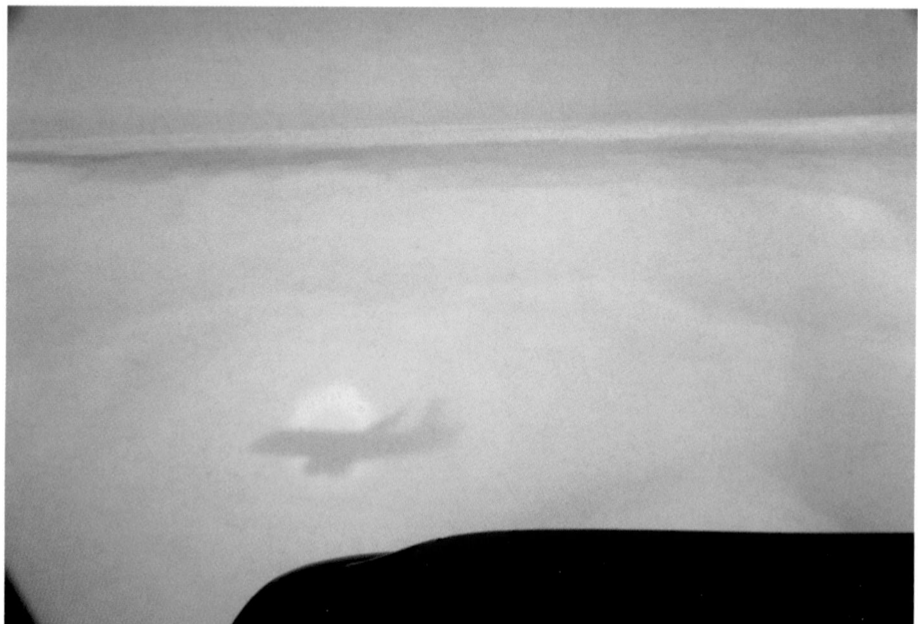

Figure 5.5 Glory with a sharp airplane shadow (BWI–LGA, 8 May 2014). The geometry indicates that I was seated just forward of the wing.

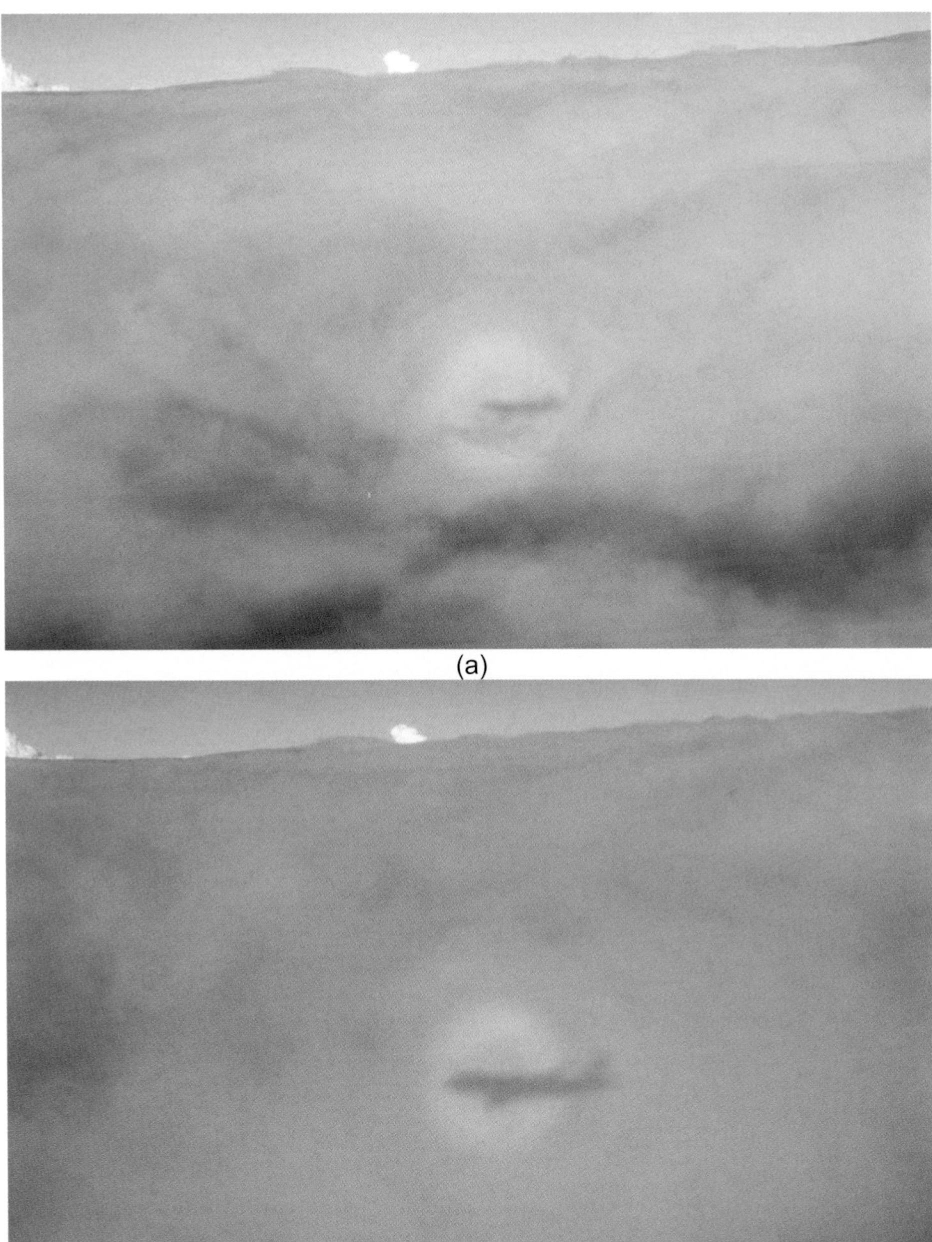

(a)

(b)

Figure 5.6 The glory remained a constant size and the airplane shadow grew larger as the airplane descended closer to the cloud (SAN–SLC, 29 Aug 2013). This photo sequence continues in Fig. 5.7.

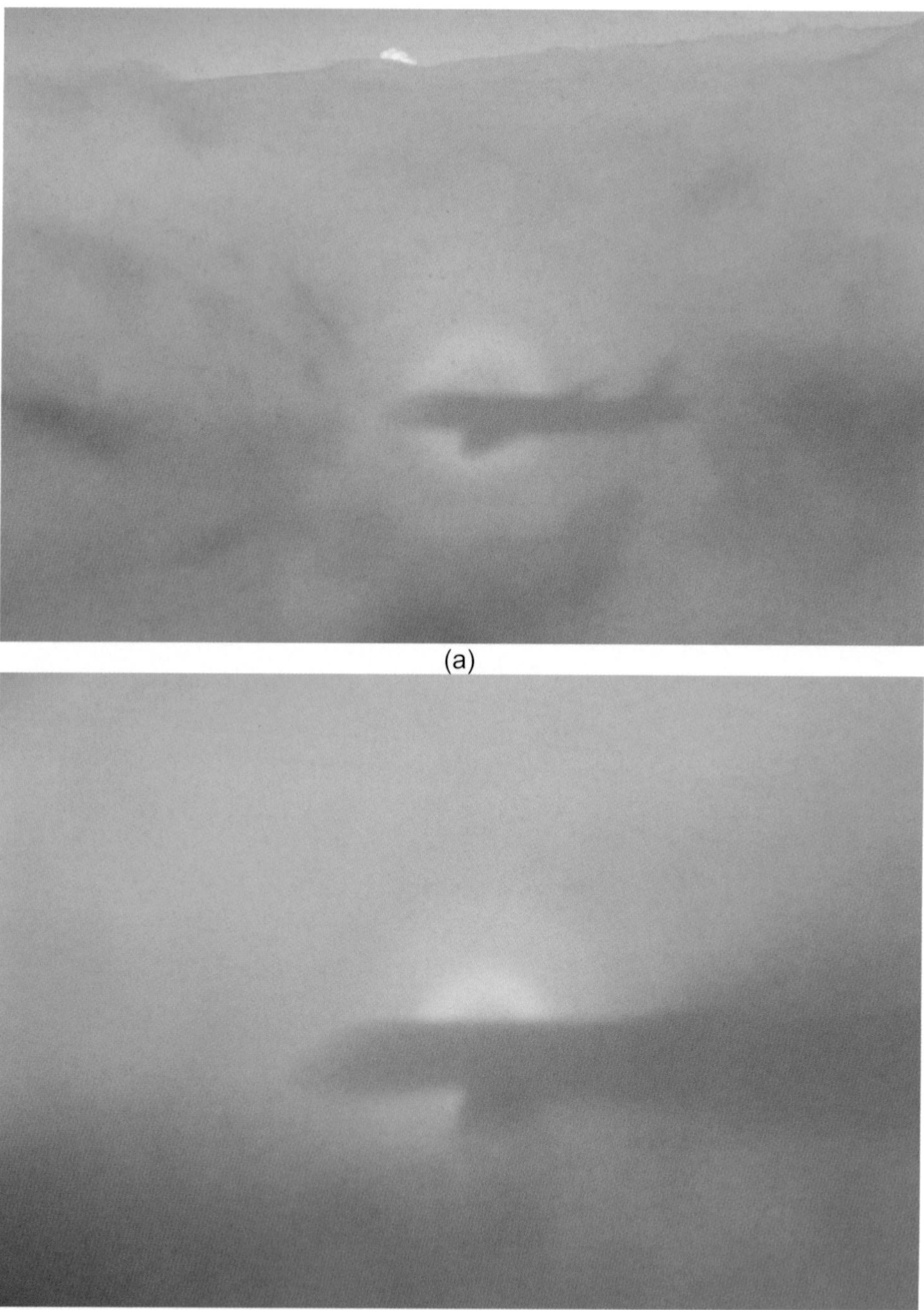

(a)

(b)

Figure 5.7 The glory remained a constant size and the airplane shadow grew larger as the airplane descended closer to the cloud (SAN–SLC, 29 Aug. 2013). This photo sequence is continued from Fig. 5.6.

5.3 Noncircular Glories

Not all real glories are perfect circles. In fact, most are not; a primary reason for this is because clouds are not uniform and do not have uniform particle sizes.[7–9] Sometimes, though, the reason is simply that the cloud is not large enough to show the entire glory, as shown in Fig. 5.8. In this case, a portion of several rings can be seen, but most of the glory would be outside the edges of this cloud. However, the situation shown in Fig. 5.9 is more complicated: This is another partial glory whose size exceeds the cloud boundaries, but here the rings flare outward at the cloud edge where the smallest cloud droplets exist (ignore the line to the left of the glory, it is a scratch in the airplane window).

The photographs in Figs. 5.10 and 5.11 show glories with ragged edges that tell us that those clouds have rapidly fluctuating droplet sizes at different points in the cloud. The regions with the largest local ring radius have the smallest droplets and the regions with the smallest local ring radius have the largest droplets. Figure 5.12 shows a glory on a cloud that apparently has an abruptly reduced droplet size in the lower left.

The glory shown in Fig. 5.13 is only a partial glory because the sunlight was only illuminating a small region between cloud layers. This partial glory also includes several discontinuous points that indicate sudden changes in droplet radius. Watching glories carefully is a great way to visualize the complexity and lack of uniformity in many clouds. It is also a great way to simply enjoy some really wonderful natural optics.

Figure 5.8 Partial glory (FAI–BRW, 11 July 2012).

Figure 5.9 Flared-loop glory (BZN–SLC, 21 Feb. 2015).

Figure 5.10 Glory with ragged edges (SLC–BZN, 22 Feb. 2010).

Figure 5.11 Glory with ragged edges (BZN–SLC, 23 Sep. 2004).

Figure 5.12 Discontinuous glory (BZN–SLC, 23 Sep. 2004).

Figure 5.13 Partial glory caused by cloud shadowing (BRW–ANC, 1 Aug. 2013).

5.4 Opposition Effect and Heiligenschein

In the gaps between clouds, if you continue to pay attention to the anti-solar point, you often will see a bright spot like that in Fig. 5.14. This spot will follow your airplane's moving shadow point on the ground below. This scenario describes the opposition effect, which is also responsible for the full moon appearing brighter than would be predicted from its brightness several nights earlier.[10] A primary cause is the lack of shadowing in the immediate vicinity of the anti-solar point.[10,11] Whether forest, grass, or even rocky ground, the average brightness consists of directly illuminated and shadowed regions. At the anti-solar point, the rays from the sun arrive directly on the surface with no shadowing, and thus in that vicinity the average brightness is higher than the surrounding partially shaded areas.[11] Other mechanisms can also contribute, including coherent backscatter[12–14] and retroreflection from crystalline rocks.[15] The opposition effect can be observed as a bright region surrounding the anti-solar point on many surfaces. Figure 5.15 is an example on tree-covered mountains, and Fig. 5.16 is an example on tundra, with the bright region surrounding the helicopter pilot/photographer's location.

Heiligenschein (German for "holy light") is a similar effect that produces a bright region around the anti-solar point because of backward scattering enhanced by the focusing of light by tiny water drops on the surface.[16–19] Figure 5.17 shows this effect around the shadow of my head on moist grass. Because of the retroreflective behavior of the heiligenschein, the camera only captured the glow around my head on the left side of Fig. 5.17, but at the time each person was observing their own private heiligenschein.

Figure 5.14 A bright spot at the anti-solar point on the desert floor, a result of the opposition effect (SLC–TUS, 12 Feb. 2014).

Figure 5.15 A bright spot at the anti-solar point on the tree-covered mountains, a result of the opposition effect (SLC–BZN, 2 Oct. 2010).

Figure 5.16 Bright spot surrounding a helicopter shadow caused by the opposition effect (North Slope of Alaska near the mouth of the Sagavonurktok River, 21 July 2016). Image printed with permission from Daniel Adams.

Figure 5.17 My own personal heiligenschein (Bozeman, MT, 12 June 2016).

Figure 5.18 Sunlight glinting on road signs with a retroreflective surface (BZN–MSP, 17 Aug. 2010).

A much stronger but similar retroreflection effect is achieved by including tiny glass beads in the paint used on road signs. Figure 5.18 shows that such signs produce bright retroreflections of the sun, even when viewed from the air. These sign glints are bright enough to be seen even from high in the air, but they become particularly impressive when closer to the ground during landing or takeoff. Whether you are at one end of your trip or in the middle, watch for these different kinds of brightening effects at the anti-solar point while waiting for the next cloud to come along and show you a beautifully colored glory.

References

1. H. C. van de Hulst, "A theory of the anti-coronae," *J. Opt. Soc. Am.* **37**, 16–22 (1947).
2. P. Laven, "How are glories formed?" Appl. Opt. 44, 5675–5683 (2005).
3. H. C. Bryant and A. J. Cox, "Mie theory and the glory," *J. Opt. Soc. Am.* **56**(11), 1529–1532 (1966).
4. S. D. Gedzelman, "Simulating glories and cloudbows in color," *Appl. Opt.* **42**(3), 429–435 (2003).
5. P. Laven, "Simulation of rainbows, coronas, and glories by use of Mie theory," *Appl. Opt.* **42**(3), 436–444 (2003).

6. P. Laven, "Atmospheric glories: simulations and observations," *Appl. Opt.* **44**, 5667–5674 (2005).
7. P. Laven, "Noncircular glories and their relationship to cloud droplet size," *Appl. Opt.* **47**(34), H25–H30 (2008).
8. J. A. Shaw and P. J. Neiman, "Coronas and iridescence in mountain wave clouds," *Appl. Opt.* **42**(3), 476–485 (2003).
9. P. J. Neiman and J. A. Shaw, "Coronas and iridescence in mountain wave clouds over northeastern Colorado," *Bull. Am. Meteorol. Soc.* **84**(10), 1373–1386 (2003).
10. B. J. Buratti, J. K. Miller, and M. Wang, "The lunar opposition surge: observations by Clementine," *Icarus* **124**(2), 490–499 (1996).
11. D. K. Lynch, "Influence of scattering surface inclination on the opposition effect," *Appl. Opt.* **54**(4), B22–B25 (2015).
12. B. W. Hapke, R. M. Nelson, and W. D. Smythe, "The opposition effect of the moon: the contribution of coherent backscatter," *Science* **260**, 509 (1993).
13. B. Hapke, R. Nelson, and W. Smythe, "The opposition effect of the moon: coherent backscatter and shadow hiding," *Icarus* **133**(1), 89–97 (1998).
14. Y. Kuga and A. Ishimaru, "Retroreflection from a dense distribution of spherical particles," *J. Opt. Soc. Am. A* **1**(8), 831–835 (1984).
15. T. S. Trowbridge, "Retroreflection from rough surfaces," *J. Opt. Soc. Am.* **68**(9), 1225–1242 (1978).
16. R. B. Myneni and E. T. Kanemasu, "The hot spot of vegetation canopies," *J. Quant. Spectrosc. Radiat. Transfer* **40**(2), 165–168 (1988).
17. S. A. W. Gerstl, "Physics concepts of optical and radar reflectance signatures," *Int. J. Remote Sensing* **11**(7), 1109–1117 (1990).
18. J. T. Enright, "Mach bands and airplane shadows cast on dry terrain," Appl. Opt. 33(21), 4723-4726 (1994).
19. A. B. Fraser, "The sylvanshine: retroreflection from dew-covered trees," *Appl. Opt.* **33**(21), 4539–4547 (1994).

Chapter 6
Shadows

6.1 Eclipses

Shadows might seem like a trivial optical phenomenon, but they actually contain a variety of brightness and color if you observe carefully.[1,2] This chapter focuses on the primary visual features that make watching shadows both entertaining and informative.

To begin, a shadow is a region of space devoid of illumination. However, the sun is not a point source but has an angular width near 0.5°, so it casts a dark shadow (the umbra) surrounded by a partially illuminated shadow (the penumbra). An exciting example is a solar eclipse (Fig. 6.1), in which the shadow of the moon blocks direct sunlight from reaching the earth.[3–7]

Figure 6.1 Solar eclipse photographed from an Alaska Air flight from Anchorage, AK to Honolulu, HI on 8 Mar. 2016. Image reprinted with permission from Dan McGlaun, eclipse2017.org.

The solar eclipse shown in Fig. 6.1 is not something we can see routinely, but it is an example of a spectacular optical display that was observed from an airplane with a major amount of advance planning and cooperation by Alaska Airlines, who adjusted the flightpath of a flight from Alaska to Hawaii to provide this spectacular view to their passengers. In this photograph, you can see the solar corona surrounding the shadowed sun (this corona is the outer atmosphere of the sun, not the corona discussed in Section 3.1), and the entire scene is wrapped in the tapered penumbra or partially shadowed region.

Figure 6.2 is a photograph from the ground of a lunar eclipse, which is when the shadow of the earth blocks direct sunlight from reaching the moon.[8–11] In this case, the moon is illuminated by a tiny amount of light that is scattered by the earth's atmosphere into the earth's umbra. The scattering process removes the blue and other short-wavelength light, leaving only orange-red light to light the moon. At a particular point during a lunar eclipse, parts of the moon can appear blue because of the absorption of yellow light by ozone high in the earth's atmosphere.[11] The eclipsed moon is a beautiful sight to see, but it is extremely dark and best photographed with a solid tripod.

Figure 6.3 is a diagram illustrating the umbra and penumbra for a lunar eclipse (a solar eclipse has similar geometry but with the earth and moon positions exchanged). The umbra is the fully shadowed region behind the earth for a lunar eclipse and behind the moon for a solar eclipse; the penumbra is the partially illuminated region between the dashed and solid lines.

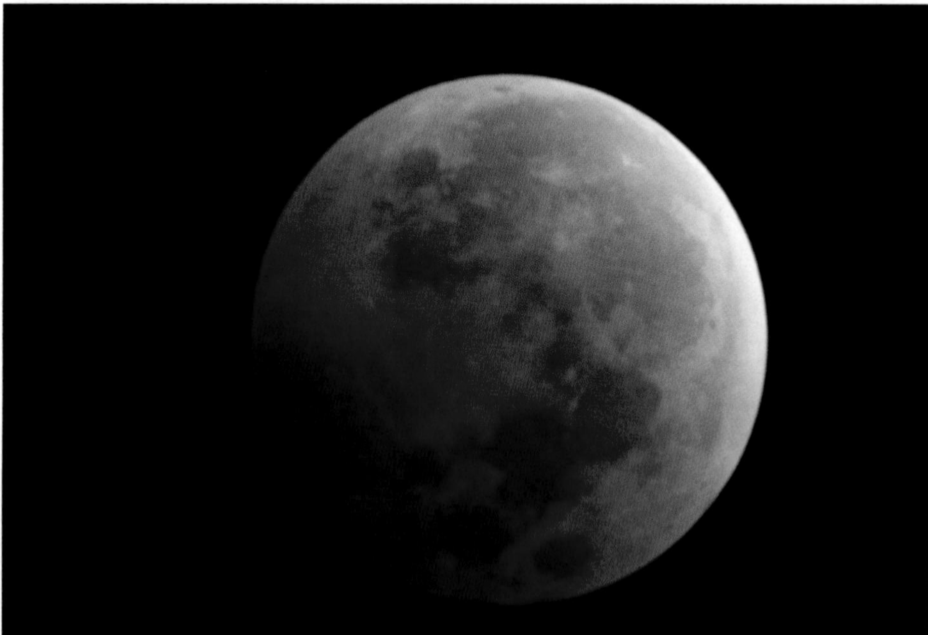

Figure 6.2 The moon illuminated with orange-red light scattered by the atmosphere into the earth's shadow during a lunar eclipse (Bozeman, MT, 8 Oct. 2014).

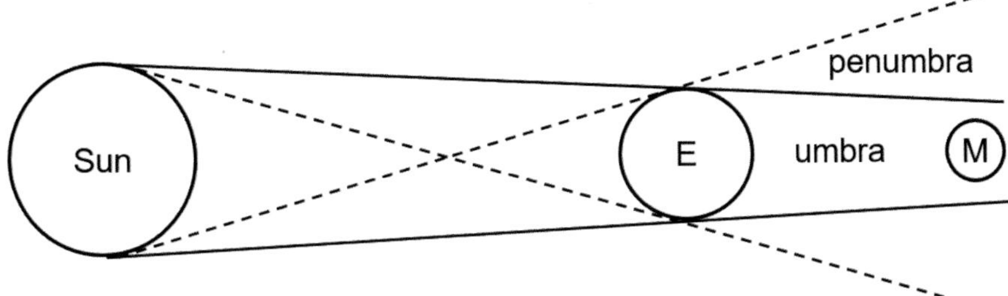

Figure 6.3 Geometry of the full shadow (umbra) and partial shadow (penumbra) regions of a lunar eclipse in which the earth (E) casts a shadow on the moon (M). The positions of the earth and moon are exchanged for a solar eclipse (not to scale).

6.2 Airplane Shadows

A far more common sight from the air is an airplane's shadow on clouds or the ground or water below (see also Section 5.2). Watching the airplane shadow can be especially interesting when it becomes distorted by being cast obliquely on a surface tilted away from the illumination direction. In Fig. 6.4(a), an airplane shadow was cast outward at a modest angle by a high sun onto a flat surface. The resulting shadow looks very much like the small jet that created it. Notice also the surface glow at the anti-solar point, an example of the opposition effect (Section 5.4). In the bottom photograph of Fig. 6.4, the descending airplane was about to land and the shadow looked pretty normal except for a little modest stretching and distortion occurring at the tail and wing.

The primary difference between the images in Fig. 6.2 is the apparent size of the shadow, which appears much larger when the airplane is closer to the ground. This is another example of how the angular size of the airplane shadow changes with distance, as we saw in Section 5.2 when the airplane shadow grew larger than the fixed-angle glory as the airplane moved closer to the clouds.

The two images in Fig. 6.5 show more extreme shadow distortion caused by a low sun on an early morning flight. This is an example of perspective, which causes us to see parallel lines as if they converge to a distant point. It gives a generally triangular shape to all shadows viewed on a surface tilted at a large angle from the illumination direction. In this case, the portions of the shadow cast on the nearest surface appear stretched the most, while the portions of the shadow cast on more distant surfaces appear less stretched. As a result, the shadow in Fig. 6.5(a) is barely stretched, while the shadow in the bottom image is extremely stretched. In fact, the shadow of the landing gear alone stretches all the way across the runway. The most extreme case is Fig. 6.6, which was taken mere seconds after Fig. 6.5. The shadow in this image is hardly recognizable as an airplane at all. The role of the surface tilt angle is illustrated in Fig. 6.7, where the shadow of the airplane body looks completely normal because it is cast on a surface lying nearly perpendicular to the illumination direction. Conversely, the bottom part of the shadow is stretched all the way across the broad runway.

(a)

(b)

Figure 6.4 (a) Airplane shadow that (b) grows larger as the airplane lands, with the high sun resulting in minimal distortion of the shadow (BZN–DEN, 1 May 2006).

(a)

(b)

Figure 6.5 (a) Airplane shadow (b) growing larger and increasingly distorted as the airplane lands while being illuminated by a low sun (BZN–SLC, 21 Sep. 2002).

Figure 6.6 Airplane shadow with extreme geometric distortion from the illumination by a low early-morning sun (BZN–SLC, 21 Sep. 2002).

Figure 6.7 Stretched shadow bottom and normal top (FAI–ANC, 1999).

6.3 Contrail Shadows

The first time you see the shadow of a contrail on the clouds below your airplane, you might mistake it for a scratch in the window. Or you might not even notice it because it can be quite narrow and hard to see. If you are on the side of the plane away from the sun, look for a dark line stretching along the cloud, ground, or water below you (Fig. 6.8). That line could be a shadow of a contrail: a long, skinny cloud formed by condensation of water vapor exiting the airplane engine. One end of the shadow marks the approximate location of your airplane, but if you are flying high above the shadowed surface, it is unlikely you will see anything but a narrow, dark shadow line. However, a lower sun angle can result in a shadow of both the contrail and the airplane being cast on a nearby cloud (Fig. 6.9). This photograph also makes it quite obvious that the contrail is indeed emanating from the airplane and not just existing as a mysterious line in space.

Once a contrail forms, it either evaporates quickly in low-humidity air or grows into a persistent contrail in higher-humidity air.[12] Persistent contrails can expand further to create cirrus clouds[13,14] Contrails sometimes expand very quickly, forming a line that is much wider than the airplane when viewed only a few airplane lengths behind the engines (Fig. 6.10). Figure 6.11 shows a sky full of contrails of various sizes—old, wide ones and fresh, narrow ones. The larger size allows expanding contrails to cast shadows that are more easily visible from a high-flying airplane. In fact, the contrail is often visible midflight without any hint of an airplane shadow on the distant surface below. Figure 6.8 is a great example of this, where no airplane shadow is visible and the left side of the contrail shadow is clearly wider than the right side (the airplane was flying left to right).

Even if the airplane shadow is not visible, you might instead find a glory at one end of the contrail shadow (Fig. 6.12, Fig. 5.4). Actually, the contrail shadow will begin some distance behind the center of the glory because it takes time for the exhaust to cool enough for the water vapor to condense. Therefore, the contrail shadow will begin some distance behind the center of the glory, which is centered at the anti-solar point (Fig. 6.12).

If you look closely at the lower-right corner of Fig. 6.13(a), you can just see a mysterious contrail shadow displaced well to one side of the glory. This situation persisted for some minutes before we passed beneath the contrail in Fig. 6.13(b). I then realized that I had been seeing a shadow of a contrail from a different airplane that had recently flown a similar route. Figure 6.14 shows another case where we can see both the contrail from another airplane and its shadow. However, with close examination of this photograph, you can just resolve the two side-by-side contrails in the sky but only a single merged shadow—probably because the nonzero angular size of the sun blurs the faraway shadow edges (see Section 5.2 and Fig. 6.3).

Figure 6.8 Contrail shadow on the water of the Prince William Sound in Alaska (ANC–SEA, 29 July 2014).

Figure 6.9 Contrail shadow and airplane shadow on a nearby cloud (SEA–OGG, 21 July 2010).

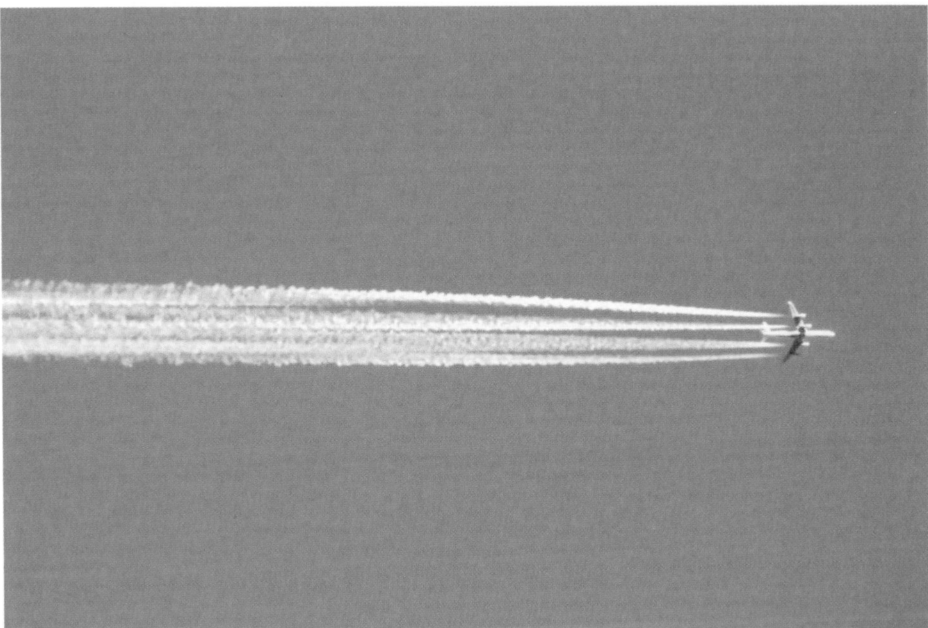

Figure 6.10 Four contrails that have merged into one much wider contrail only a few airplane lengths behind the engines (Draper, UT, 18 March 2009).

Figure 6.11 Contrails of various widths (Tremonton, UT, 26 June 2016).

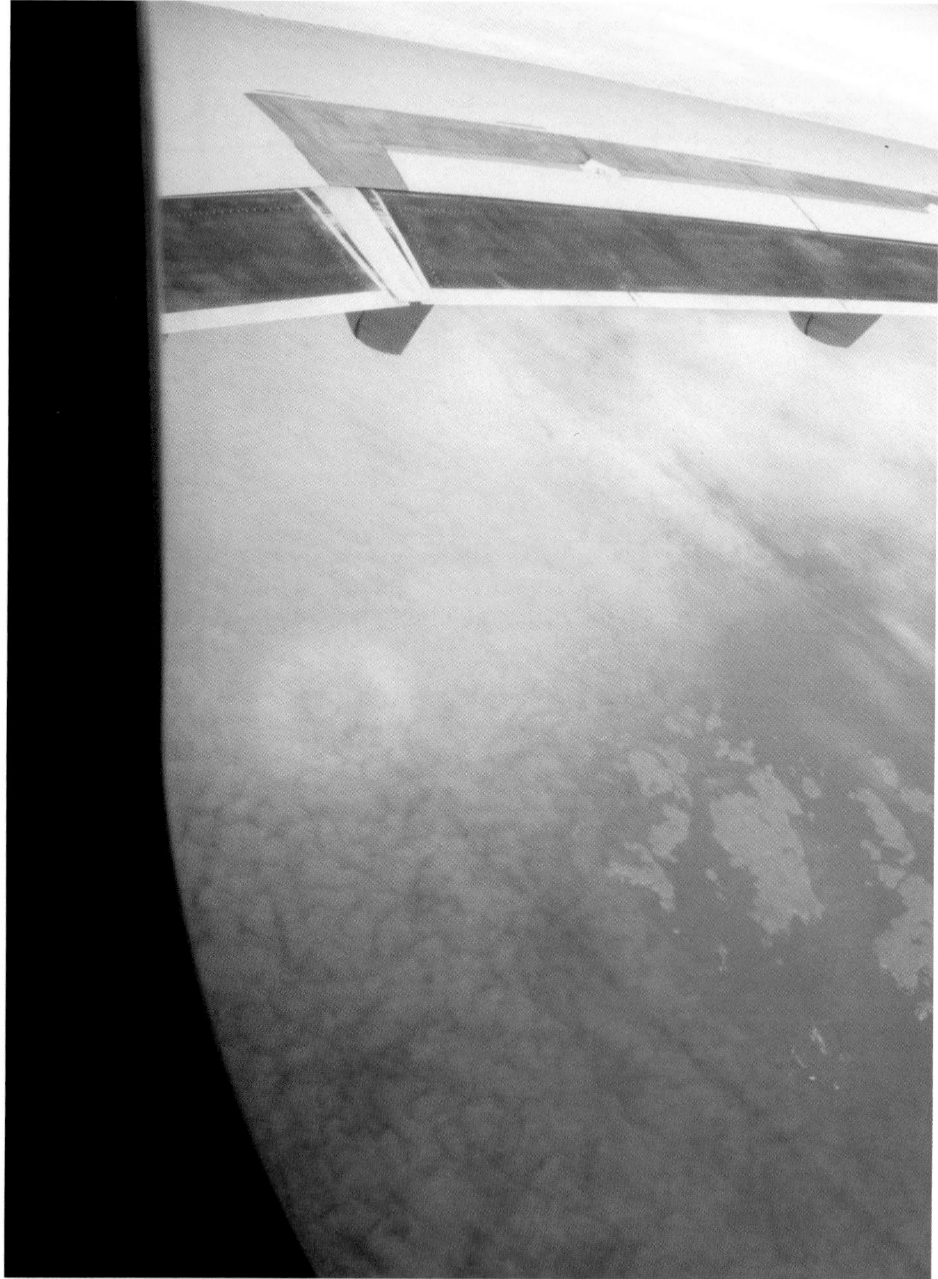

Figure 6.12 Contrail shadow beginning at the edge of a glory (SEA–ANC, 13 March 2005).

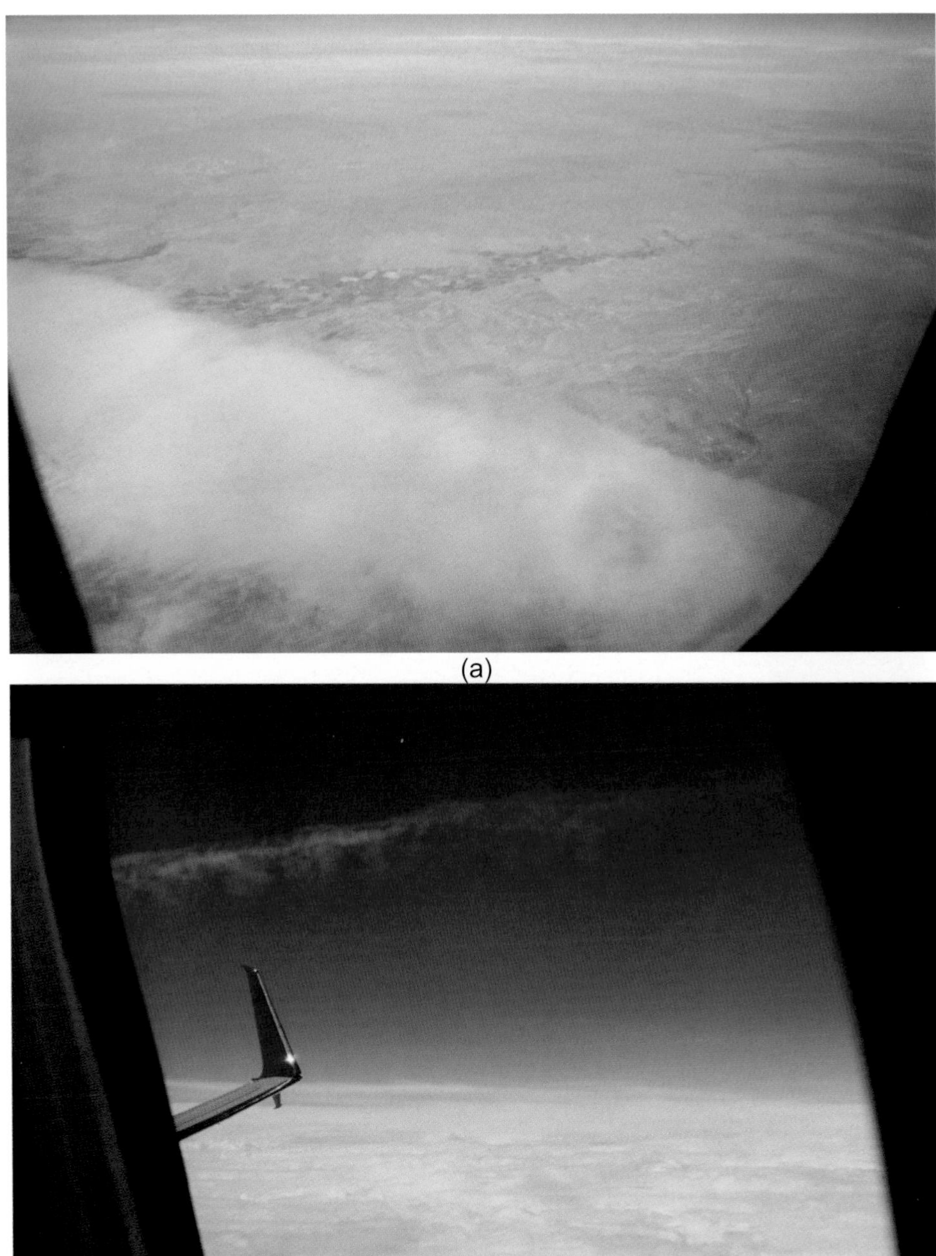

(a)

(b)

Figure 6.13 (a) Glory with a mysteriously displaced contrail shadow; (b) contrail from another plane that cast the shadow (SLC–SEA, 10 June 2015).

Figure 6.14 Contrail from an earlier airplane and shadow (BZN–SEA, 4 April 2016).

6.4 Mountain Shadows

An airplane provides a unique vantage point from which you can see both a mountain and its shadow. Regardless of the mountain, its shadow will approach a triangle because of perspective. The apex of the shadow triangle marks the anti-solar point, so a glory there is also possible, as in Fig. 6.15. Notice the triangular shadows of the mountain and the photographer in this photograph (also called a Brocken spectre). Figure 6.16 is a photograph I took of the shadow of both Denali and its immediate neighbor, Mt. Foraker (Denali is the tallest mountain in North America at 6,190 m, and Foraker is not far behind at 5,304 m). This particular shadow is actually a composite of two triangles. If you look closely you can see a small light spot indicating a gap between the Denali shadow on the right and the Foraker shadow on the left.

Even if the mountains you happen to see do not tower as high as Foraker and Denali, near sunrise or sunset their shadows can stretch far and assume impressive shapes that resemble sharp, jagged teeth (Fig. 6.17). Their shadows can stretch across the ground (Fig. 6.17) or into the clouds and haze (Fig. 6.16).[15]

Figure 6.15 Triangular mountain shadow with glory around the shadow of the photographer and the mountain peak (near Juneau, AK, June 2016). Image printed with permission from Paul Neiman.

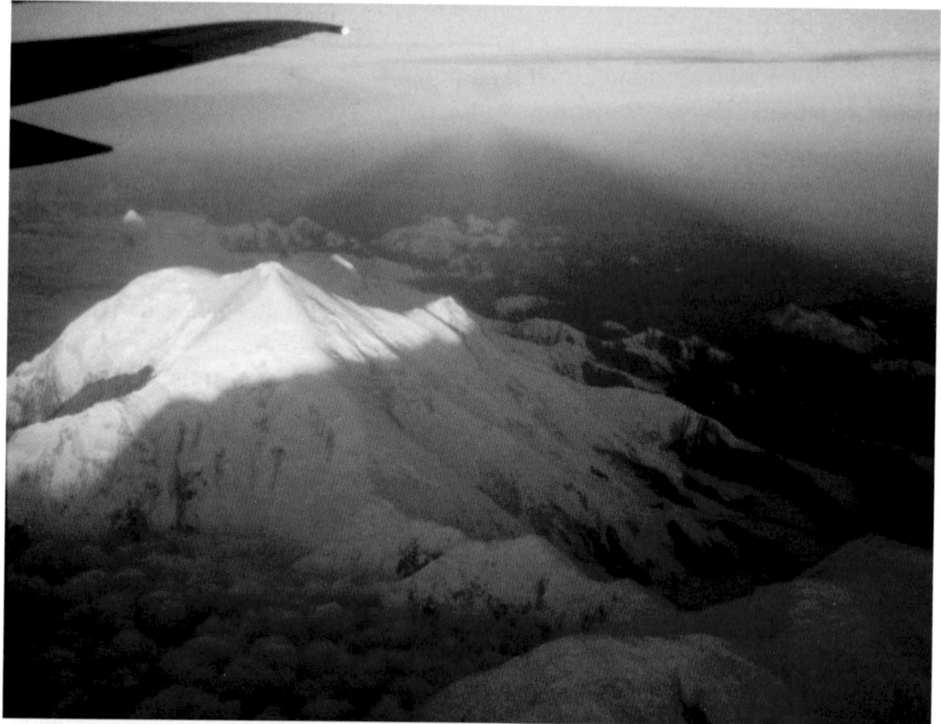

Figure 6.16 Triangular mountain shadow of Denali (FAI–ANC, Aug. 1999).

Figure 6.17 Triangular mountain shadows (TUS–SLC, 24 Feb 2015).

6.5 Cloud Shadows

Clouds also cast shadows, which can make nice places to sit on a hot day (Fig 6.18). These shadows are, of course, as varied in shape and size as the clouds that cast them. When the sun is high in the sky and the clouds are well separated, it is easy to visually connect each cloud with its shadow. At times when the clouds are more complex or the sun is shining on them more obliquely, the shadows can look quite different from the clouds. When cast on water, cloud shadows can take on the appearance of a bloom of something dark in the water (Fig. 6.19). This is an excellent way to observe how much of the water color comes from the scattering of direct sunlight (see Section 7.1).

6.6 Crepuscular and Anticrepuscular Rays

Crepuscular and anticrepuscular rays are fancy words for beams of light from the sun or moon that shine through gaps between clouds, extending downward or upward in the sky.[15–20] Both types emanate from the sun, but you see crepuscular rays by looking toward the sun (Figs. 6.20–6.22) and anticrepuscular rays by looking toward the anti-solar point, away from the sun (Figs. 6.23–6.25). Like all scattered sunlight, crepuscular rays look white when the sun is high, i.e., light traverses a short atmospheric path (Fig. 6.20), and yellow or orange when the sun is low, i.e., light traverses a longer atmospheric path (Fig. 6.21).

Figure 6.18 Cloud shadows (MSP–BZN, 19 May 2010).

Figure 6.19 Cloud shadows on water (HNL–SEA, 26 May 2008).

Figure 6.20 Crepuscular rays flooding through gaps in the clouds alongside a patch of sun glitter on the Great Salt Lake (SAN–SLC, 20 Aug. 2014).

Figure 6.21 Crepuscular rays made yellow by scattering in the long atmospheric path from the low sun (FAI–MSP, 7 Aug. 2013).

The hardest to see are subtle pink rays that rise high into the pre-dawn or post-sunset twilight sky (Fig. 6.22). The pink color occurs when light made red by scattering in a long path mixes with the deep blue light of the twilight sky. These pink rays are formed by faraway clouds located beyond the visible horizon from the observer's location.

Because light from the sun is nearly collimated, crepuscular rays are parallel to each other but appear to fan out from the sun because of perspective. Anticrepuscular rays are the same kind of beams of light, viewed on the opposite horizon. They are also parallel light rays, but because of perspective appear to converge toward the anti-solar point. They can be extensions of crepuscular rays that cross the entire sky or beams of light shining through gaps in clouds closer to the horizon opposite the setting or rising sun. They are generally more difficult to see than crepuscular rays. Both crepuscular and anticrepuscular rays can be perceived as either bright beams of light shining through gaps between clouds or as dark shadows of clouds on an otherwise bright sky. Which way you perceive the rays depends on how the light is distributed in the sky. For example, both Figs. 6.23 and 6.24 could be interpreted as dark cloud shadows or as bright rays between the dark regions. However, Fig. 6.25 is quite obviously a large cloud shadow extending toward the anti-solar point.

6.7 Earth's Shadow

Section 2.2 discussed the colors of sunrise and sunset, and introduced the earth's shadow, as well. The latter is literally a shadow of the earth that appears as a dark

Figure 6.22 Pink crepuscular rays before sunrise (BZN–SLC, 25 Sep. 2015).

Figure 6.23 Anticrepuscular rays on the south–southeast horizon of Fairbanks, AK, with the late-evening sub-Arctic summer sun setting to the north–northwest (BRW–FAI, 14 July 2012).

Figure 6.24 Anticrepuscular rays on the eastern horizon at sunset (MSP–BNA, 10 Aug. 2014).

Figure 6.25 Triangular cloud shadow that can be interpreted as a large anticrepuscular ray (MSP–MCO, 27 April 2011).

Figure 6.26 Earth's shadow at sunrise (BZN–SLC, 27 Feb. 2015).

Figure 6.27 Earth's shadow at sunset after moonrise (AMS–MSP, 11 Jan. 2014).

band on the horizon opposite the sun. It rises opposite the setting sun and sets opposite the rising sun. It is usually fringed by a band of pink or orange light on the top that is sunlight reddened by scattering mixed with twilight blue. It can stretch across a large portion of the horizon, as shown in Fig. 6.26. The pink light seemingly below the shadow in this photograph is actually pink sunrise light illuminating clouds closer to the airplane. Figure 6.27 shows an orange fringe that is part of the anti-twilight arch or Belt of Venus[21] (see Section 2.2 and Fig. 2.10).

Figure 6.28 Giant cloud shadow (crepuscular ray) that resembles the earth's shadow (SLC–BWI, 17 May 2010).

The photograph in Fig. 6.28 looks a lot like the earth's shadow and occurred as the sun set behind my eastbound aircraft. However, it was too close to the setting sun to be the earth's shadow, and at the time I took the photograph it was notably elevated above the southern horizon. This must be a giant cloud shadow, essentially a dark crepuscular ray, arising from clouds below the western horizon.

References

1. D. K. Lynch, "Shadows," *Appl. Opt.* **54**(4), B154–B164 (2015).
2. M. E. Churma, "Blue shadows: physical, physiological, and psychological causes," *Appl. Op*t. **33**(21), 4719–4722 (1994).
3. J. M. Pasachoff, "Solar eclipses as an astrophysical laboratory," *Nature* **459**(7248), 789–795 (2009).
4. J. Mottmann, "Solar eclipse predictions," *Am. J. Phys*. **48**(8), 626–628 (1980).
5. G. E. Shaw, "Sky brightness and polarization during the 1973 African eclipse," *Appl. Opt.* **14**(2), 388-394 (1975).
6. S. D. Gedzelman, "Sky color near the horizon during a total solar eclipse," *Appl. Opt.* **14**(12), 2831–2837 (1975).

7. G. P. Können and C. Hinz, "Visibility of stars, halos, and rainbows during solar eclipses," *Appl. Opt.* **47**(34), H14–H24 (2008).

8. S. D. Gedzelman and M. Vollmer, "Simulating irradiance and color during lunar eclipses using satellite data," *Appl. Opt.* **47**(34), H149–H156 (2008).

9. N. Hernitschek, E. Schmidt, and M. Vollmer, "Lunar eclipse photometry: absolute luminance measurements and modeling," *Appl. Opt.* **47**(34), H62–H71 (2008).

10. M. Vollmer and S. D. Gedzelman, "Simulating irradiance during lunar eclipses: the spherically symmetrical case," *Appl. Opt.* **47**(34), H52–H61 (2008).

11. S. D. Gedzelman and M. Vollmer, "Twice in a blue moon," *Weatherwise* **62**(5), 28–35 (2009).

12. Environmental Protection Agency, *Contrails Factsheet*, EPA430-F-00-05, https://www3.epa.gov/otaq/regs/nonroad/aviation/430f00005.pdf (2000).

13. D. J. Travis, "Variations in contrail morphology and relationships to atmospheric conditions," *J. Weather Mod.* **28**(1), 50–58 (1996).

14. F. Schröder, B. Kärcher, C. Duroure, J. Ström, A. Petzold, J.-F. Gayet, B. Strauss, P. Wendling, and S. Borrmann, "On the transition of contrails into cirrus clouds," *J. Atm. Sci.* **57**(4), 464–480 (2000).

15. J. L. Monteith, "Crepuscular rays formed by the Western Ghats," *Weather* **41**(9), 292–299 (1986).

16. D. K. Lynch, "Optics of sunbeams," *JOSA-A* **4**(3), 609–611 (1987).

17. S. D. Gedzelman and M. Vollmer, "Crepuscular rays: laboratory experiments and simulations," *Appl. Opt.* **50**(28), F141–F152 (2011).

18. M. S. Van Den Broeke, W. H. Beasley, and M. B. Richman, "The role of atmospheric conditions in determining intensity of crepuscular and anticrepuscular rays," *Monthly Weather Review* **138**(7), 2883–2894 (2010).

19. S. D. Gedzelman and M. Vollmer, "Atmospheric optical phenomena and radiative transfer," *Bull. Am. Meteorol. Soc.* **89**(4), 471–485 (2008).

20. M. Zinkova, "Rays in the fog," *Weather* **67**(1), 3 (2012).

21. R. L. Lee, Jr., "Measuring and modeling twilight's Belt of Venus," *Appl. Opt.* **54**(4), B194–B203 (2015).

Chapter 7
Water Colors and Glitter

7.1 Water Colors

An airplane provides great opportunities to view the colors and patterns of light scattered and reflected from water. Pure water lit by sunlight appears blue when it is deep enough that you do not see light reflected from the bottom (Fig. 7.1).[1–3] Shallow water near the middle of Fig. 7.1 and in Fig. 7.2 allows light reflected from the bottom to mix with the scattered blue light, creating shades of blue-green and green. The dark patches are either regions of cloud shadow (Fig. 6.19) or shallow regions with a darker-colored underwater surface.

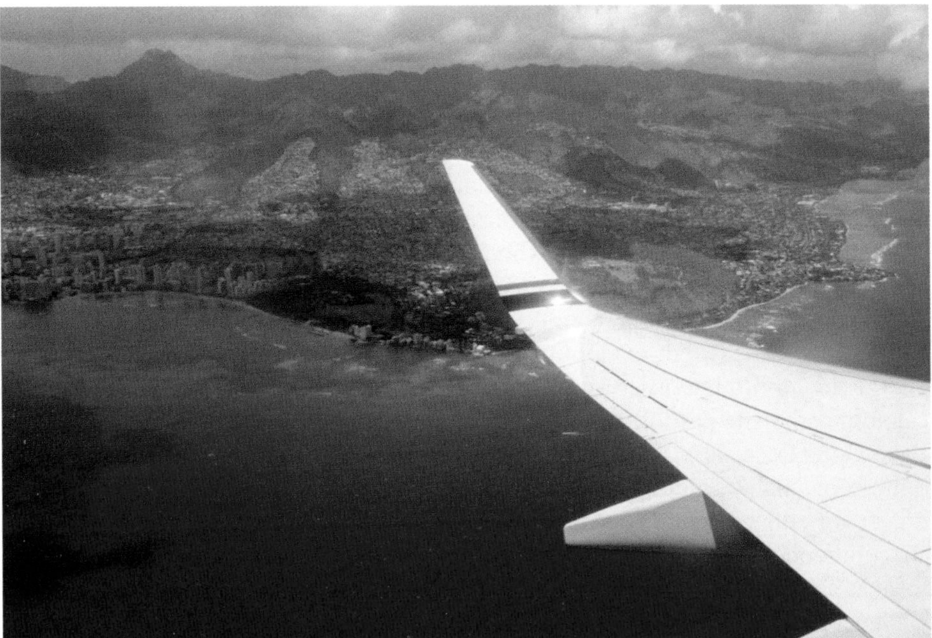

Figure 7.1 Pure blue color of deep water and green color of shallow water near Honolulu, HI (HNL–SEA, 26 May 2008).

Figure 7.2 Clean water that appears green because of the scattering and absorption of sunlight (KOA–HNL, 26 May 2008).

Figure 7.3 is a plot of the scattering coefficient (dashed line) and absorption coefficient (solid line) for pure water,[2,4] showing that the pure blue color of deep water is the result of scattering from water molecules (very similar to scattering by air molecules) and that red light is removed by absorption.[5–7] The vivid colors that can be seen in hot pools of water at Yellowstone Park result from the same mechanisms but with greater variety due to the microbial mats that coat the surfaces of all but the hottest thermal pools.[2,3] The water color is not influenced strongly by the sky color except when viewing water near the horizon, at which angle the surface strongly reflects skylight.[1,2]

Water also can assume a milky green appearance from scattering by small suspended particles. For example, the famous turquoise-green color of Bear Lake on the Idaho–Utah border is primarily a result of scattering from suspended calcium carbonate particles (Fig. 7.4). Similarly, the milky green color of Blanca Lake in the Cascade Mountains of Washington State is caused by the scattering of light from small particles of glacial till (Fig. 7.5). The green swirls in the satellite image of the Barents Sea (Fig. 7.6) are the result of scattering from coccolithophores and possibly other phytoplankton—tiny micro-organisms that form an important component at the bottom of the marine food chain.[8]

Large quantities of silt carried down from the Alaska Range turn the water of the Tanana River in central Alaska brown (Fig. 7.7). An incredible billowing pattern can be seen from up close at the point where the silt-laden Tanana River meets the smaller and clearer Chena River (Fig. 7.8). A less turbulent mixing of silty brown water with the milky green water of Bear Lake is seen in Fig. 7.9.

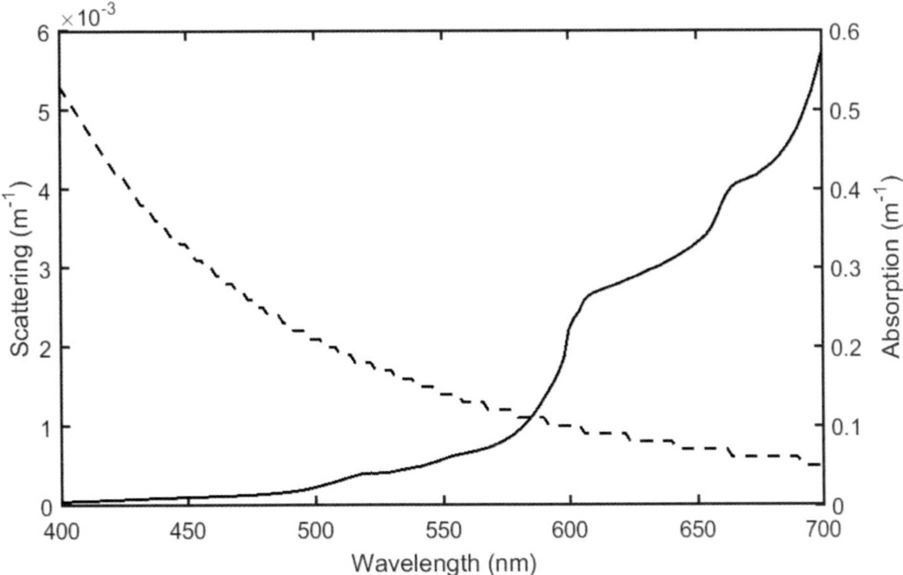

Figure 7.3 Pure-water scattering coefficient (dashed line) and absorption coefficient (solid line).[2,4]

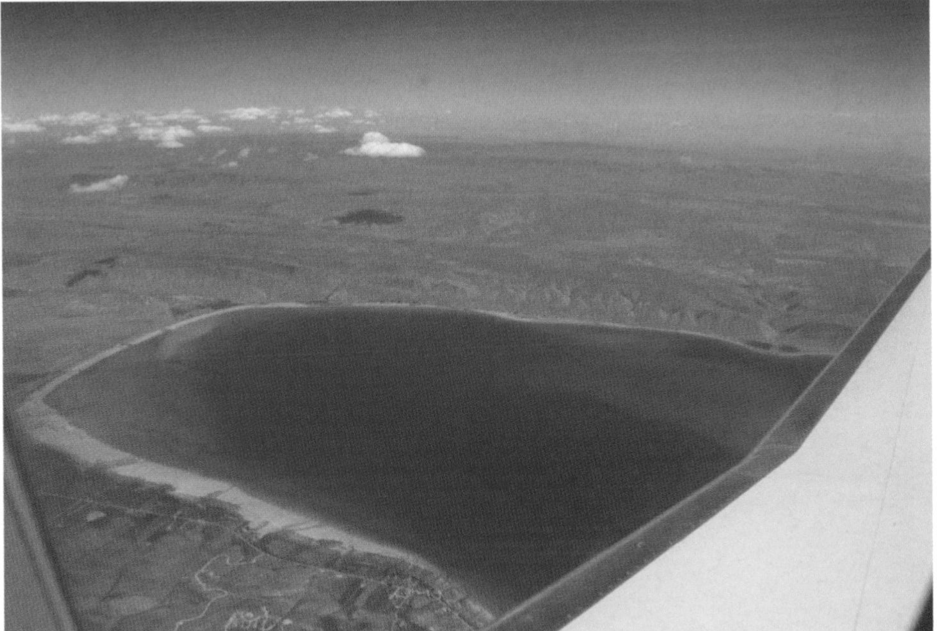

Figure 7.4 Water that appears turquoise green because of scattering by calcium carbonate particles (SLC–BZN, 21 June 2006).

Figure 7.5 The milky green color of Blanca Lake in the Cascade Mountains is a result of scattering from glacial till in the water (BZN–SEA, 21 July 2010).

Figure 7.6 Blue water with green swirls caused by scattering from coccolithophores and possibly other phytoplankton in the Barents Sea (MODIS satellite image courtesy of NASA, 14 Aug. 2011).

Figure 7.7 Water with a large quantity of glacial silt in the Tanana River outside Fairbanks, AK (FAI–BRW, 11 July 2012).

Figure 7.8 Turbulent mixing of silty water from the Tanana River into the clearer water of the Chena River (Fairbanks, AK, 6 Aug. 2013).

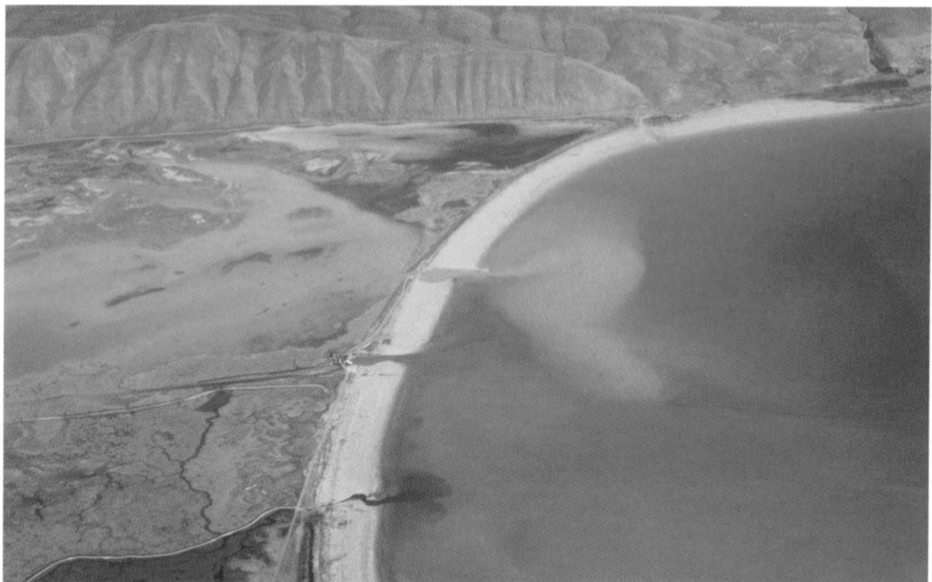

Figure 7.9 Brown water mixing into turquoise-green water in Bear Lake on the Utah–Idaho border (SLC–BZN, 21 June 2006).

From the air we also can observe the pattern of water freezing and melting. Ponds and lakes freeze and thaw starting at the outer edge where the shallower water is more rapidly heated by sunlight [Fig. 7.10(a)]. When not contaminated by wind-blown soil or black-carbon aerosols, ice and snow appear white on top but deep blue inside. The interior blue color is a result of absorption removing red light (red absorption is approximately five times stronger than blue absorption).[9] There is also strong scattering inside ice, but it serves primarily to increase the optical path length, thereby increasing the net effect of absorption. The blue color seen in holes or pools in ice and crevasses in glaciers is caused by this effect and not reflected sunlight [Fig. 7.10(b), Fig. 7.11].

7.2 Water Waves

The largest water waves have gravity as a restoring force and carry most of the mechanical energy. Tiny capillary waves, with surface tension as a restoring force, have the steepest slopes and create the glitter patterns discussed in Section 7.3. Because of the high altitude of most flights, even large waves breaking on the shore are best seen during takeoff and landing (Fig. 7.12). At flight altitude, whitecaps on the open ocean (Fig. 7.13) can be seen as a white-speckled blue ocean surface. It is also possible, but less common, to see a surface manifestation of internal waves propagating along density gradients within the water (Fig. 7.14). Internal waves are gravity waves that exist within the water, not on its surface, supported by a discontinuity in a water property, such as temperature or salinity. When I took the photograph in Fig. 7.14, we were shooting a laser beam into the water from an airplane to measure internal waves.[10]

(a)

(b)

Figure 7.10 Water in solid form as ice: (a) Minnesota lakes melting inward from the outside (SDF–MSP, 2 April 2009) and (b) Alaskan glaciers emptying into the Prince William Sound (ANC–SEA, 14 March 2011).

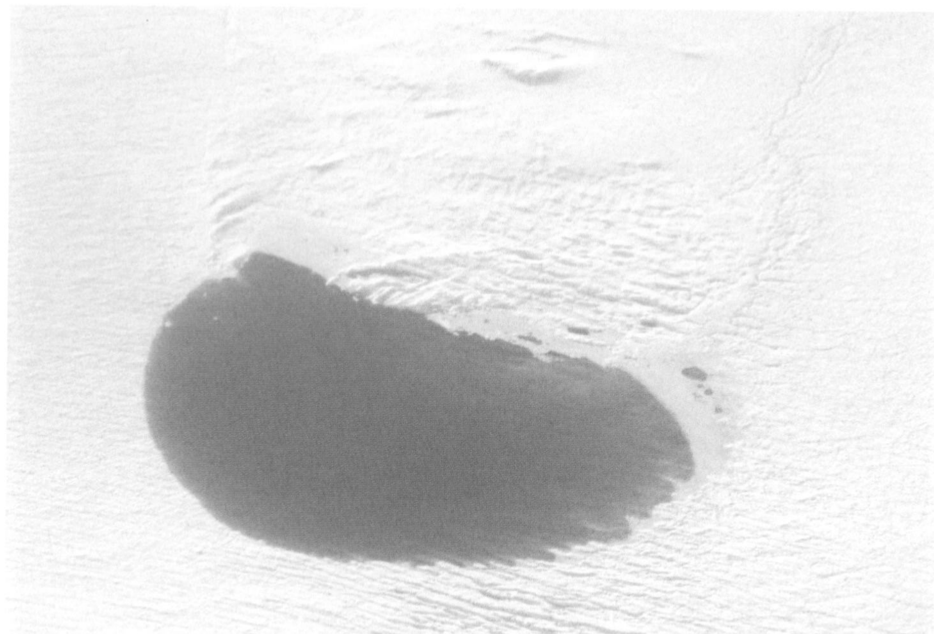

Figure 7.11 Blue pools of water on top of sea ice (ANC–FRA, 9 Aug. 2013). Image printed with permission from Michael Vollmer.

Figure 7.12 Gravity waves breaking on the beach near Narita, Japan, photographed during takeoff (HND–KOJ, 25 March 2016).

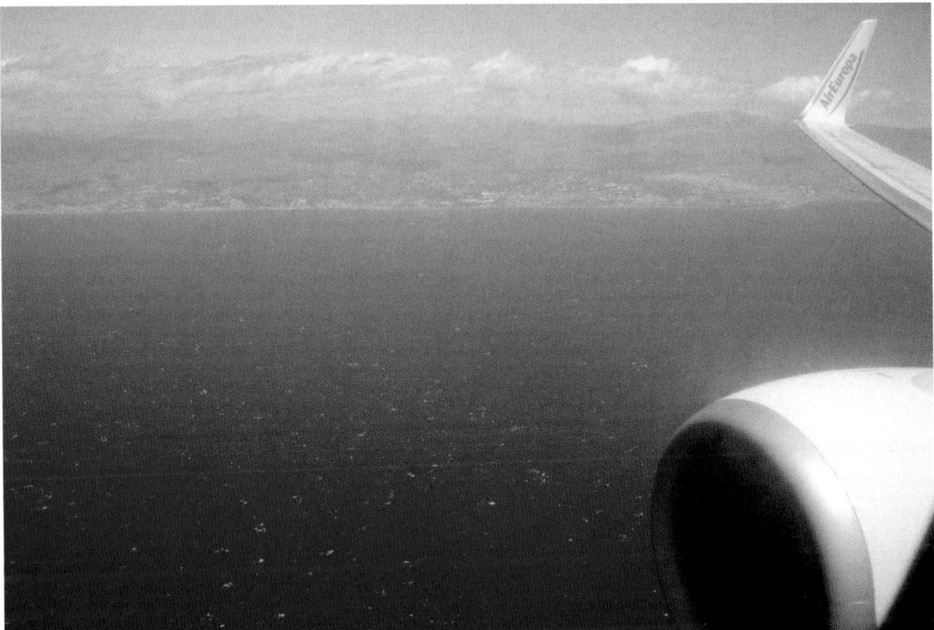

Figure 7.13 Whitecaps on the ocean photographed off the coast of Malaga, Spain (CDG–AGP, 28 May 2016).

Figure 7.14 Internal waves photographed from a research aircraft (East sound, WA, 16 Sep. 2011).

7.3 Water Reflections

Light reflecting from water can produce fascinating effects. When the wind is calm but there are mild disturbances on the water surface, such as a child or dog playing on one side of a pond or a boat moving slowly through a channel, look for reflections of the surrounding scenery. Slowly undulating waves can create "fun-house mirror" reflections of the sky and nearby scenery (Fig. 7.15) or of a low-flying airplane.[11] Each reflection is seen on the portion of the wave that is angled just right to act like a mirror for that particular piece of the background. From the air, well-defined reflections of clouds can be seen on smooth water (Fig. 7.16). These reflections are not particularly bright because at angles below 50° the water reflects less than 5% of the incident light, so they are most visible when the direct sunlight is blocked by some of the clouds.

When the waves are not so systematically generated as they were by the slow-moving boat that created Fig. 7.15, portions of the sky are reflected into quasi-circular patterns called light loops. The photograph in Fig. 7.17 shows dark loops surrounded by yellow-orange fringes. The dark rings are reflections of the dark shoreline around the water, while the yellow-orange fringes are reflections of the sunset colors (the wider view in Fig. 7.18 provides context for interpreting the light loops in Fig. 7.17). Light loops can be particularly enjoyable to watch from up close during sunrise or sunset, when the sky takes on such a rich variety of colors. This is an optical effect that is best viewed close-up, but the reflection of the sun or moon from water produces many wonderful patterns of light that can be enjoyable to observe from the air.

Figure 7.15 Specular reflections of scenery from a wavy water surface (Orcas Island, WA, 18 June 2013).

Figure 7.16 Cloud reflections on smooth water (BZN–SEA, 9 April 2015).

Figure 7.17 Light loops on water with reflected sunset colors (Fukuoka, Japan, 28 March 2016).

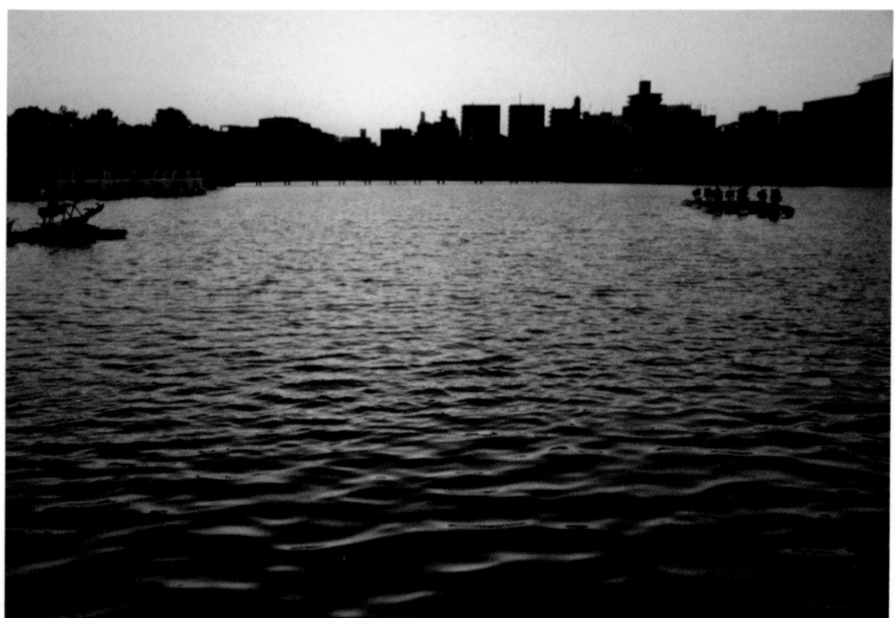

Figure 7.18 Wider view of the scene containing the light loops shown in Fig. 7.17 (Fukuoka, Japan, 28 Mar. 2016).

7.4 Glints and Glitter

A perfectly calm water surface generates a single reflection of the sun at the specular point where the incident light angle is equal to the reflected light angle. This kind of single mirror-like reflection (called a glint) is shown in Fig. 7.19 on a smooth water surface in a sheltered cove, adjacent to open water where rippled water reflects a more complex set of glints called a glitter pattern. Most glints are seen from small capillary waves that last only as long as the wind is blowing.[11–13]

A glitter pattern is a collection of many individual glints, each a reflection from a tiny wave facet tilted at the angle for a specular reflection at that location (Fig. 7.20). Photographs of sun glitter patterns have been used to measure wave-slope statistics and wind speed.[14] My colleague and I later used a laser to create glitter patterns that could be seen under cloudy skies and found that even with constant wind speed a water surface becomes more highly rippled when the water is warmer than the nearby air.[15] We also found that glints were a fractal process whose fractal dimension carries information about the surface roughness.[16]

When viewed from above, reflections of a high sun from a wind-rippled water surface form an oval-shaped glitter pattern (Fig. 7.21). The oval becomes elongated as the sun (or moon) drops lower in the sky, eventually matching the width of the sun with a length that is related to the maximum wave slope. The light forming a glitter pattern can assume a yellow or orange color when the bluish light is removed by scattering along a long atmospheric path (Figs. 7.22–7.24). Looking at any of these glitter patterns up close allows you to see the individual glints (Fig. 7.25).

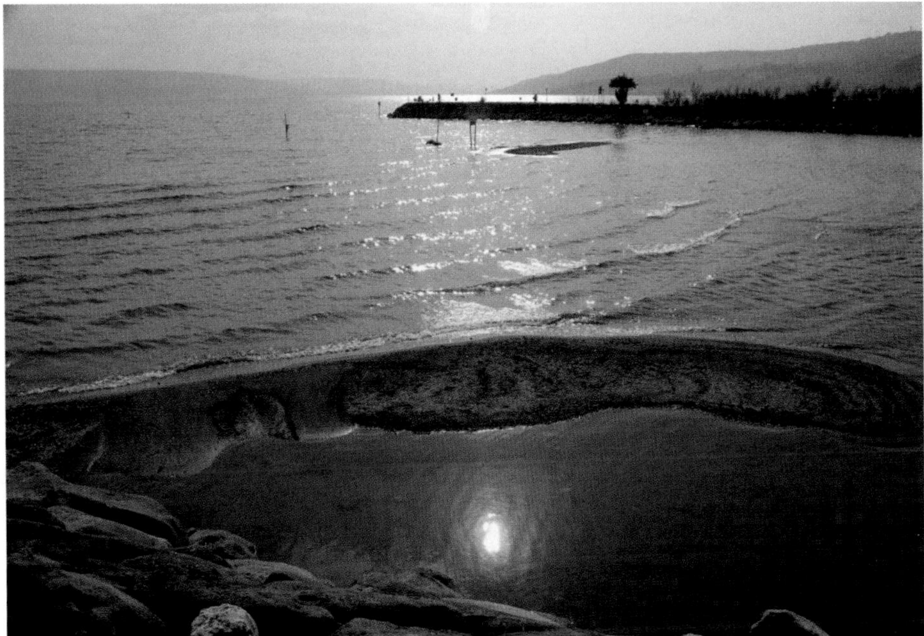

Figure 7.19 Single glint on smooth water and multiple glints on rippled water (Sea of Galilee, Israel, 4 Jan. 2014).

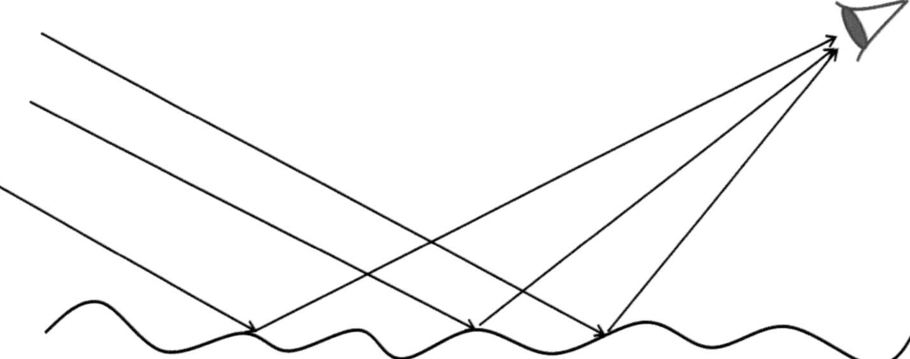

Figure 7.20 A glitter pattern results from specular (mirror-like) reflections of the sun from multiple points on a water surface, each with a different slope. This phenomenon is similar to the light pillar generated by sun reflections from tilted ice crystals (see Fig. 8.22).

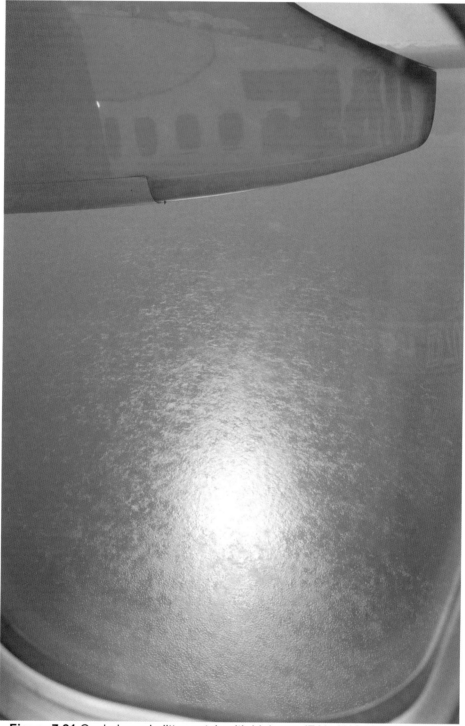

Figure 7.21 Oval-shaped glitter patch with high sun (FAI–ANC, 29 July 2014).

Figure 7.22 Orange glitter path formed by the low, setting sun reflecting from many small tilted waves on the ocean (SAN–SLC, 13 Sep. 2013).

Figure 7.23 Yellow glitter pattern formed by the setting sun reflecting from many small tilted waves on the ocean (CDG–TLV, 31 Dec. 2013).

Figure 7.24 Glitter pattern with orange fading to yellow at the near end where the atmospheric path length is shortest (ANC–FRA, 9 Aug. 2013). Image printed with permission from Michael Vollmer.

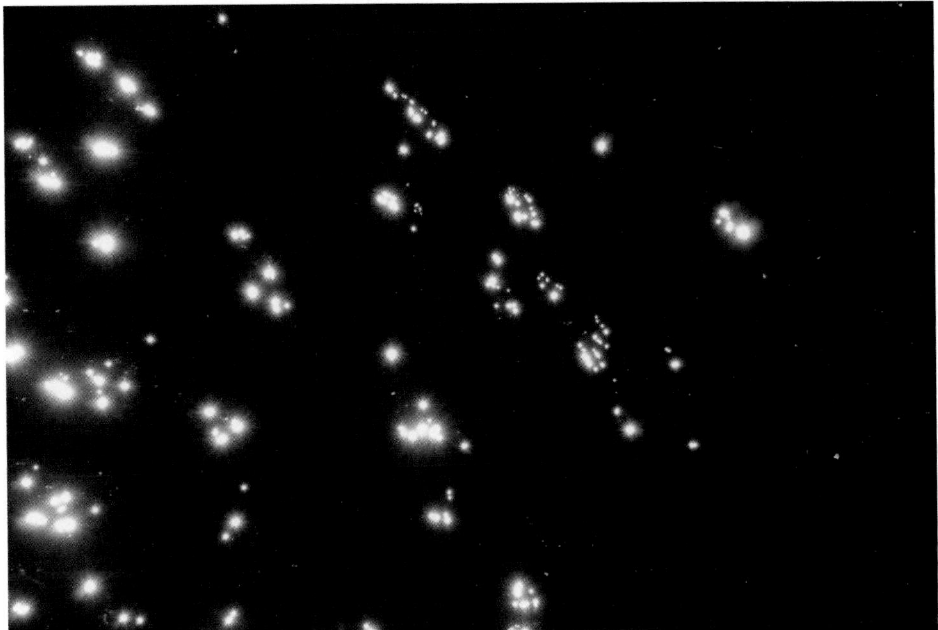

Figure 7.25 Each glitter pattern is a collection of individual glint points (San Juan Island, WA, 17 June 2013).

Light from any source can reflect from water and create a glitter pattern, including the sun, moon, street lights, or lighted signs. Even a bright reflection of the sun can act as the source for a glitter pattern where one is otherwise not expected. Figure 7.26 is an example of a bright glitter pattern whose source was a reflection of the sun from a curved reflective building. In this photograph, you can clearly see the individual glints at the front of the glitter pattern. The rest of the pattern also contains many individual glints that are not easily distinguished by the eye. Not only can this kind of architecture lead to nice glitter patterns, but it can also focus light and cause sunburns or hot spots for unsuspecting visitors.[17]

A glitter pattern becomes more complex when larger waves modulate and systematically distort the otherwise random capillary waves. This scenario can lead to kinks or bends in glitter paths, and it can significantly alter the oval shape we would otherwise expect for a high-sun glitter pattern. An example of this is shown in Fig. 7.27, where boat wakes induced a systematic pattern onto the randomly distributed capillary-wave glitter pattern. On the right side of this photograph we see a surface slick suppressing wind-blown capillary waves, resulting in a darker smooth area on the water surface.

Multiple light sources can create multiple simultaneous glitter patterns. For example, I photographed the series of glitter patterns in Fig. 7.28 from an airplane preparing to take off after a severe-weather delay at the Denver airport. The heavy rain had left enough water on the runway that it developed tiny wind-induced capillary waves that created these glitter patterns.

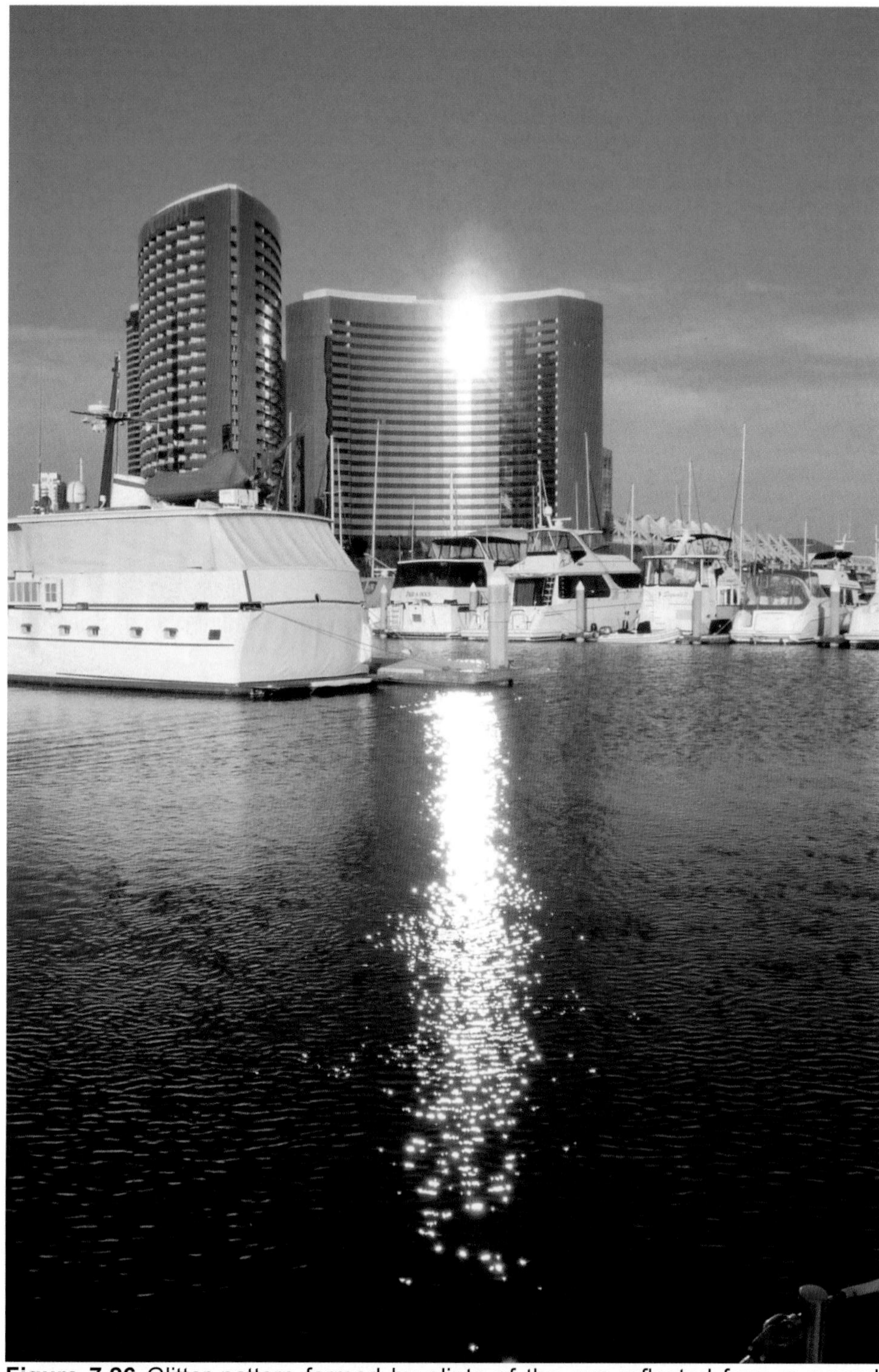

Figure 7.26 Glitter pattern formed by glints of the sun reflected from a curved building (San Diego Bay, CA, 14 Aug. 2012).

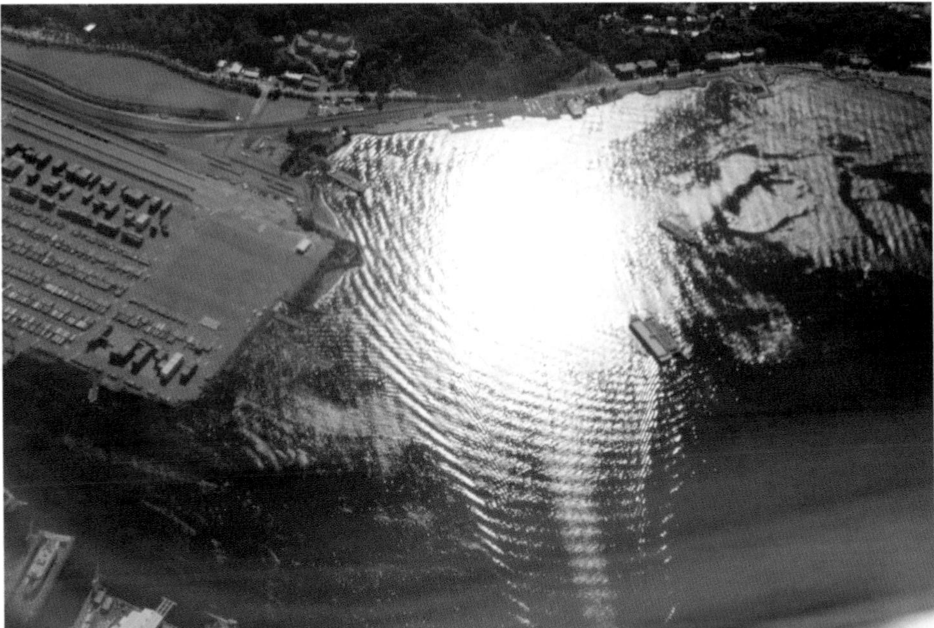

Figure 7.27 Broad and varied glitter pattern showing boat wakes (SEA–OGG, 21 July 2010).

Figure 7.28 Multiple glitter patterns formed by reflections of airport lights from wind waves on the wet runway (DEN–SLC, 9 June 2015).

References

1. G. N. Plass, T. J. Humphreys, and G. W. Kattawar, "Color of the ocean," *Appl. Opt.* **17**(9), 1432–1446 (1978).
2. P. W. Nugent, J. A. Shaw, and M. Vollmer, "Colors of thermal pools at Yellowstone Park," *Appl. Opt.* **54**(4), B128–B139 (2015).
3. J. A. Shaw, P. W. Nugent, and M. Vollmer, "Colors of the Yellowstone thermal pools for teaching optics," *Proc. SPIE* **9793**, 97031S (2015).
4. H. Buiteveld, J. H. M. Hakvoort, and M. Donze, "The optical properties of pure water," *Proc. SPIE* **2258**, 174–182 (1994).
5. R. C. Smith and K. S. Baker, "Optical Properties of the clearest natural waters," *Appl. Opt.* **20**, 177–184 (1981).
6. A. Morel et al., "Optical properties of the 'clearest' natural waters," *Limnol. Oceanogr*, **52**(1), 217–229 (2007).
7. D. Mobley, "Optical properties of water," Chapter 43 in *Handbook of Optics*, Vol. I, 2nd ed., M. Bass, E. W. Van Stryland, D. R. Williams, and W. L. Wolfe, eds., McGraw Hill, New York (1995).
8. T. J. Smyth, T. Tyrrell, and B. Tarrant, "Time series of coccolithophore activity in the Barents Sea, from twenty years of satellite imagery," *Geophys. Res. Lett.* **31**(11), DOI: 10.1029/2004GL019735 (2004).
9. C. F. Bohren, "Colors of snow, frozen waterfalls, and icebergs," *J. Opt. Soc. Am.* **73**(12), 1646–1652 (1983).
10. J. H. Churnside et al., "Airborne lidar detection and characterization of internal waves in a shallow fjord," *J. Appl. Rem. Sens.* **6**(1), 063611 (2012).
11. E. J. Walsh et al., "Visual demonstration of three-scale sea-surface roughness under light wind conditions," *IEEE Trans. Geosci. Rem. Sens.*.**43**(8), 1751-1762 (2005).
12. J. A. Shaw, "Glittering light on water," *Optics and Photonics News* **10**(3), 43–45, 68 (1999).
13. D. K. Lynch, D. S. P. Dearborn, and J. A. Lock, "Glitter and glints on water," *Appl. Opt.* **50**(28), F39–F49 (2011).
14. C. Cox and W. Munk, "Measurement of the roughness of the sea surface from photographs of the Sun's glitter," *J. Opt. Soc. Am.* **44**(11), 838–858 (1954).
15. J. A. Shaw and J. H. Churnside, "Scanning-laser glint measurements of sea-surface slope statistics," *Appl. Opt.* **36**(18), 4202–4213 (1997).
16. J. A. Shaw and J. H. Churnside, "Fractal laser glints from the ocean surface," *J. Opt. Soc. Am. A* **14**(5), 1144–1150 (1997).
17. M. Vollmer and K.-P. Möllmann, "Caustic effects due to sunlight reflections from skyscrapers: simulations and experiments," *Eur. J. Phys.* **33**(5), 1429–1455 (2012).

Chapter 8
Halos and Pillars

8.1 Refraction in Ice Crystals

Ice crystals produce a wonderful variety of optical phenomena in the atmosphere. These effects can arise from the refraction (bending) of light rays passing through crystals, reflections from ice crystal faces, or a combination of both.[1–6] This chapter opens with a discussion of the optical effects produced by refraction in ice crystals. Figure 8.1 is a simulation from the HaloSim program[6] that summarizes the main halos discussed in this chapter. Refer to it as you read about parhelia or sundogs (Section 8.1.1), 22° halos (Section 8.1.2), upper and lower tangent arcs (Section 8.1.3), subsuns and pillars (Section 8.2), and 46° halos and related arcs (Section 8.3). The figure also shows several halo arcs not discussed here.[1–6]

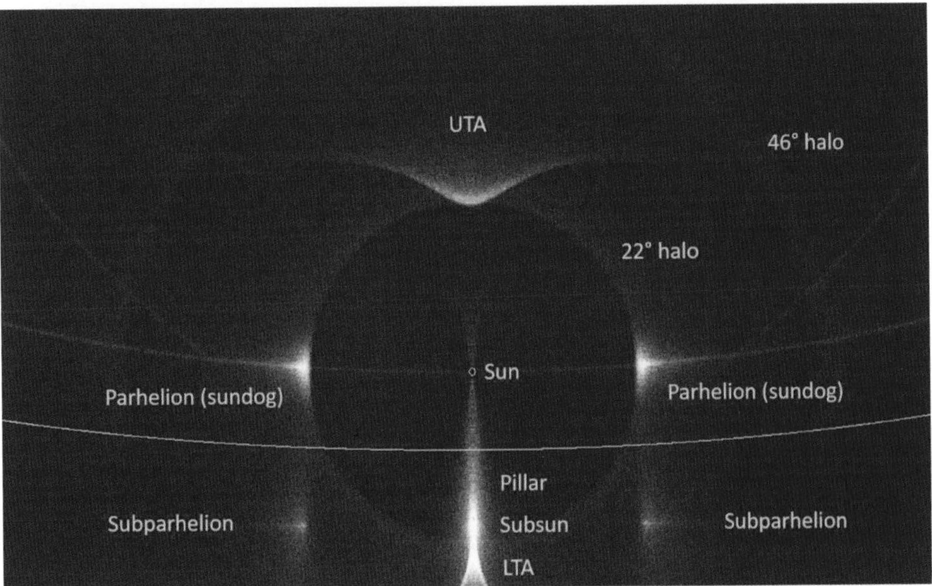

Figure 8.1 Simulation showing the halos discussed in this chapter. The solid white line marks the horizon, the circle marks the location of the sun, UTA is the upper tangent arc, and LTA is the lower tangent arc. Figure created with the HaloSim software,[6] © L. Cowley & M. Schroeder, all rights reserved.

8.1.1 Sundogs or parhelia

On the sunward side of an airplane, watch for patches of white or colored light appearing on one or both sides of the sun or moon (Figs. 8.2–8.5). These are parhelia, commonly called sundogs. No one seems to know for sure the source of the name "sundog," but there has been speculation of a source in mythology.[7]

Figure 8.2 Sundog (parhelion) 22° to the right of the sun (ABQ–SLC, 5 Nov. 2015).

Figure 8.3 Close-up view of a right-side sundog (TUS–SLC, 19 Feb. 2013).

Figure 8.4 Sundogs on both sides of the sun (TUS–SLC, 19 Feb. 2013).

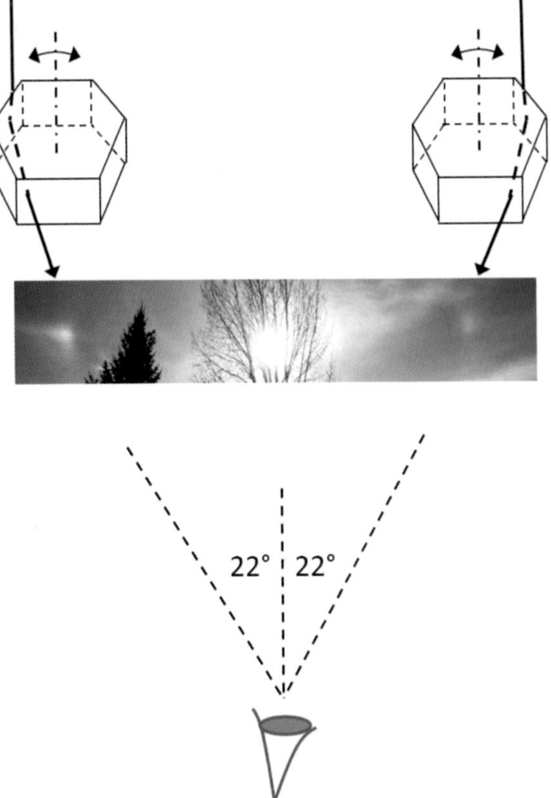

Figure 8.5 Geometry for viewing sundogs 22° on either side of the sun.

It does not need to be cold on the ground to see ice-optics phenomena in high clouds; in fact, I have seen many sundogs and halos in deserts and semi-tropical places because of the frequent presence of cirrus clouds. Even if the air near the surface is quite hot, it can be exceedingly cold at the high altitudes of cirrus clouds. In the absence of a temperature inversion, the air temperature in the lower level of the atmosphere, called the troposphere, becomes colder as the altitude increases (Fig. 8.6). The altitude where temperature begins to increase again (the tropopause) marks the beginning of the next-higher atmospheric layer, called the stratosphere.

In the troposphere, air cools with altitude at a rate of approximately 7 °C/km. Therefore, even on a hot day with a surface air temperature of 40 °C, a cirrus cloud at a 10-km altitude will have a temperature near –30 °C. Ice crystals can form at temperatures below 0 °C, although there is a strong variation of crystal shapes and sizes with both temperature and humidity.[8–11] The basic building block of ice crystals is a hexagon, based on the shape of the water ice molecule. The two most common forms of ice crystals in nature, which can explain most of the observable halo effects, are the hexagonal plate and column crystals (Fig. 8.7). There are other crystal shapes in nature, but the simplest crystals produce the best halos.

When light enters one side face of a hexagonal plate crystal and exits another, it is refracted (or bent) by an amount that depends on the wavelength. Blue light is bent slightly more than red light, but all of the refracted light clusters near the minimum deviation angle of 22°. This is the same effect that can be observed in a 60° prism (Fig. 8.8). However, natural halos exhibit less color than a laboratory prism because of crystal imperfections, variations in the crystal refractive index, and, perhaps most importantly, overlapping colors from multiple crystals with different angular orientations. Furthermore, colors from rays above the minimum-deviation angle overlap so that we see a fringe of red on the inside with a flare of bluish-white light on the outside of a typical sundog (Figs. 8.2–8.4).

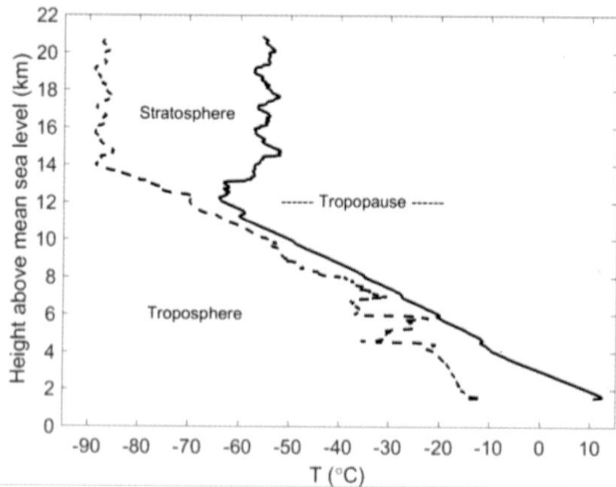

Figure 8.6 Air temperature (solid line) and dewpoint (dashed line) vs. height measured by a weather balloon above Montana State University (Bozeman, MT, 15 April 2014). Clouds can exist wherever the two lines are close together, indicating high relative humidity.

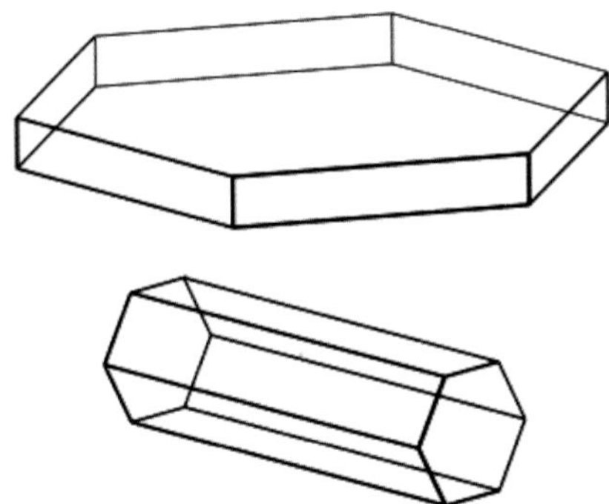

Figure 8.7 Hexagonal plate and column ice crystals (courtesy of Dave3457 [public domain], via Wikimedia Commons).

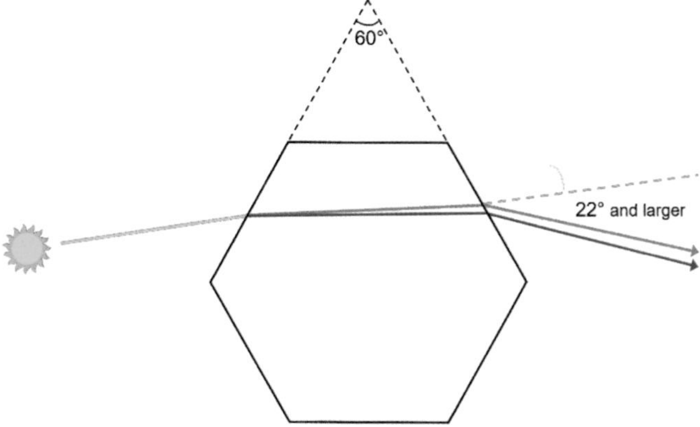

Figure 8.8 Hexagonal plate crystal with 60° prism ray paths that create a sundog (the tan line represents white light from the sun).

8.1.2 22° halo

Crystals tend to fall with their longest dimension horizontal (you can observe this by dropping paper cutouts). Therefore, when hexagonal plate crystals fall in calm, cold air, an observer can see sundogs or moondogs located 22° to the side(s) of the sun or moon (Figs. 8.2, 8.4, and 8.5). Slightly wobbling crystals elongate the sundog vertically (Fig. 8.2). In more turbulent air, the crystals begin to tumble, and the resulting collection of randomly oriented plate crystals spread light into a full circle with a 22° angular radius: the 22° halo (Figs. 8.9–8.11), which is rarer than simple ray tracing suggests because of the rounded edges and hollow or otherwise complex forms of real ice crystals.[12–14] Similar hexagonal crystals also produce colorful sparkles, sundogs, or halos on the top of a layer of snow.[15]

Most halos are much less bright and colorful than predicted by the simplest models because most real ice crystals are too complicated and imperfect, and many ice crystal clouds are too thick and block too much light.[16,17] Halos are brightest when clouds block roughly 1–75% of the sunlight. Any more and the sky turns gray. But the cloud can be optically thin and still produce a bright halo in a blue sky with near-perfect crystals (which are more likely in thin clouds).[16–19]

The photographs in Figs. 8.9–8.11 illustrate the variety of brightness and color that occur in 22° halos with clouds of differing thickness. Figure 8.9 is a nearly colorless halo formed in a thick cloud, whereas Fig. 8.10 is a slightly more colorful halo in a cloud that appears to have a slightly higher transmission. Figure 8.10 also exhibits brightening at the sundog positions. Figure 8.11 shows how much more colorful a 22° halo can be when it forms in an optically thin cloud with a blue sky background. This is also a great example of the extra effort that is sometimes required to photograph a full optical display through a small airplane window. From the confines of my airplane seat, I could not position my head low enough to see the top of this halo. Therefore, to capture the full halo in the picture, I first photographed the piece I could see easily to determine the proper exposure settings, and then I photographed the full halo by holding the camera near chest level and pointing it up at the window.

Because the 22° halo photographs shown so far were all taken with a very wide-angle lens, you may not realize just how large this halo really is. It is a circle of 22° radius and therefore 44° diameter. Even though this is only about half the size of a full primary rainbow, it still is an impressively large circle of light in the sky. If the bottom of a 22° halo is at the horizon, the top will be half way up to the top of the sky. A typical cellphone camera might just capture the full circle of the 22° halo or crop the circle on the shorter axis of the image. With a full-frame 35-mm DSLR camera, you would need a wide-angle lens with a focal length of about

Figure 8.9 Nearly colorless 22° halo in a thick cloud (SEA–BZN, 6 Feb. 2014).

Figure 8.10 More colorful 22° halo in a thick cloud (SEA–OGG, 21 July 2010).

30 mm or shorter to capture the full 22° halo. The photographs shown here were taken with the following full-frame 35-mm camera lenses: 46 mm for the single sundog in Fig. 8.2; 75 mm for the close-up sundog view in Fig. 8.3; 30 mm for the full halo view in Fig. 8.4; 16-mm fisheye for Fig. 8.9; 27 mm for Fig. 8.10; and 16-mm fisheye for Fig. 8.11. A more conventional view of a 22° halo seen through a small airplane window without a wide-angle lens is shown in Fig. 8.12. This photograph also shows how badly the window can impair your view and how the best colors appear where the cloud is optically thin.

Sometimes only a portion of the halo can be seen in the part of the sky containing the requisite ice crystals. An example of this is the partial 22° halo shown in Fig. 8.13, together with a nice glitter pattern on the ocean below. Note also that halos are partially polarized.[20–23]

Some hexagonal column crystals have tapered ends that create a six-sided pyramid (Fig. 8.14). Whereas simple plates and columns have only 60° and 90° angles, these more complex pyramidal crystals provide 28°, 52.4°, 56°, 62°, 63.8°, and 80.2° angles that can refract light to create remarkable multiple-ring concentric halos, called odd-radius halos. Figure 8.15 is an example that shows at least the 22°, 18°, and 9° halos (other displays have been documented with twice this number of concentric halos[24,25]). The number and brightness of concentric halos is determined in part by the presence and size of the various pyramidal crystal faces.

8.1.3 Upper and lower tangent arcs

When the sun is not too high in the sky, V-shaped winged arcs appear at the top of a 22° halo and two foot-like appendages extend down from the bottom of the 22°

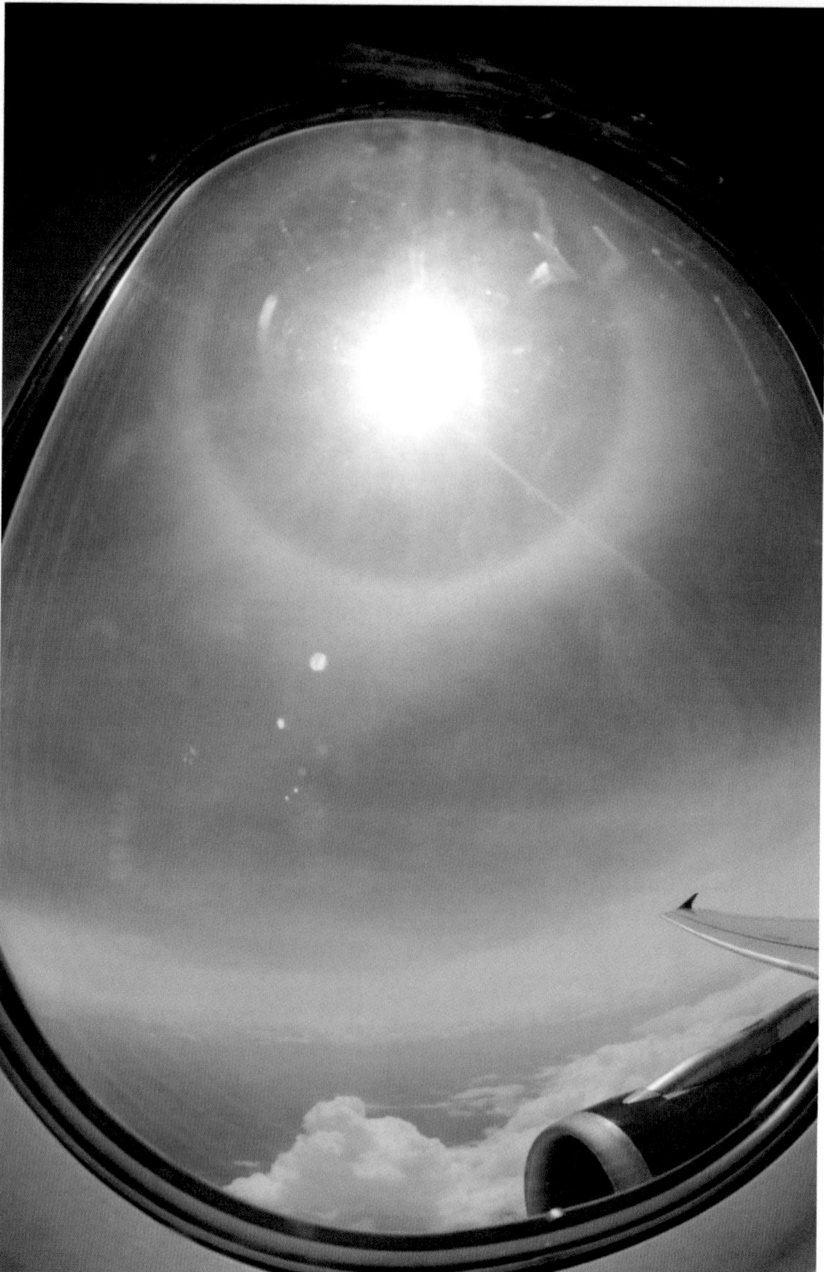

Figure 8.11 Fisheye photograph of a 22° halo observed in high, thin clouds on a trip to Spain (BZN–MSP, 27 May 2016).

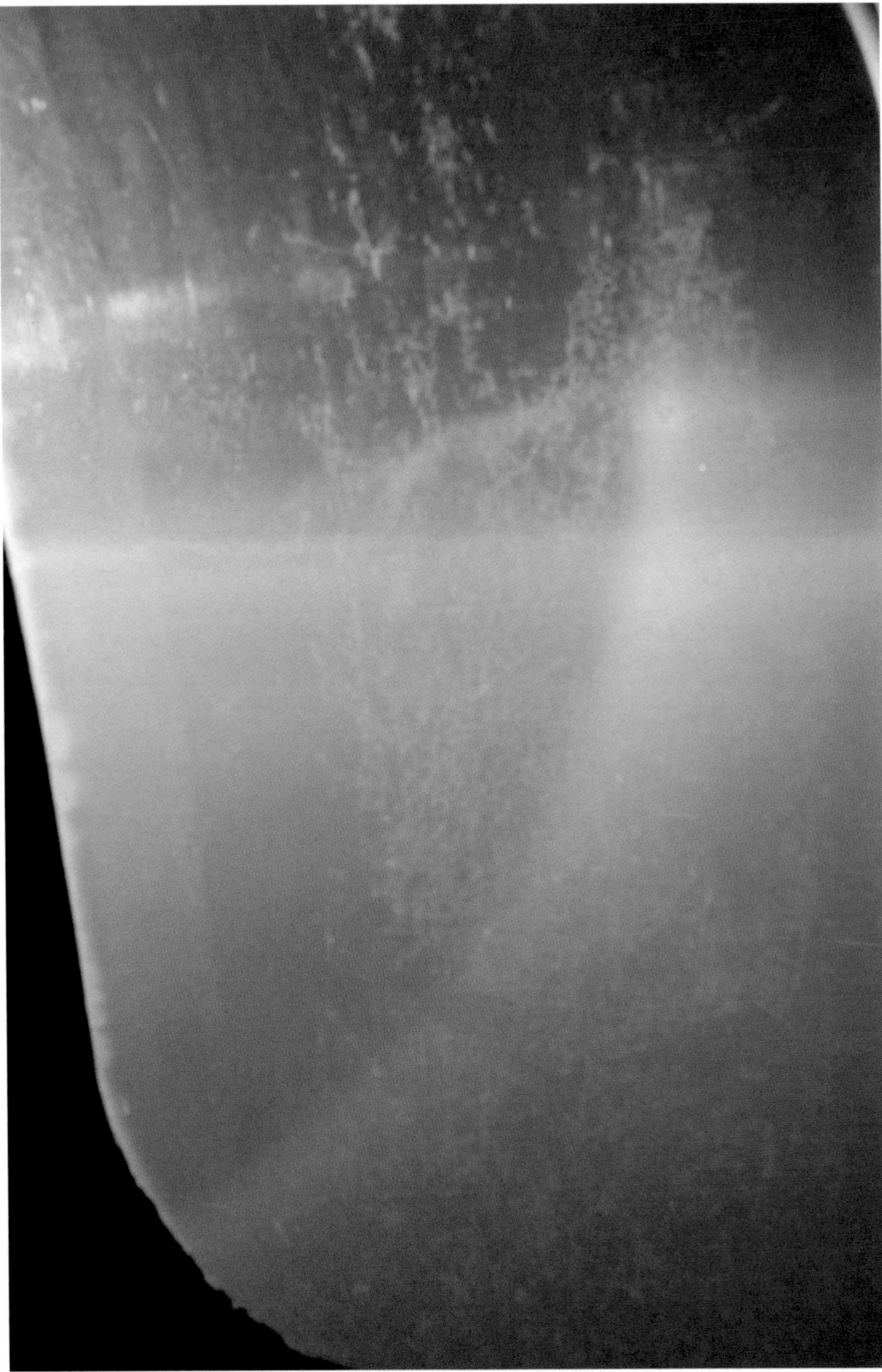

Figure 8.12 Common appearance of a 22° halo without a wide-angle lens and with a badly scratched window (ROC–MSP, 21 June 2011).

Figure 8.13 Partial 22° halo and glitter pattern on the ocean (ANC–FRA, 9 Aug. 2013). Image printed with permission of Michael Vollmer.

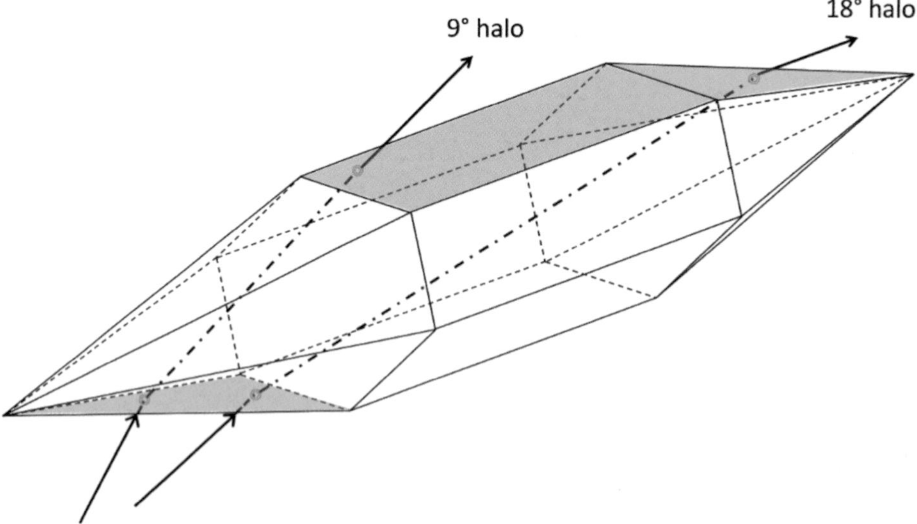

Figure 8.14 Pyramidal crystal ray paths that create some of the odd-radius halos.

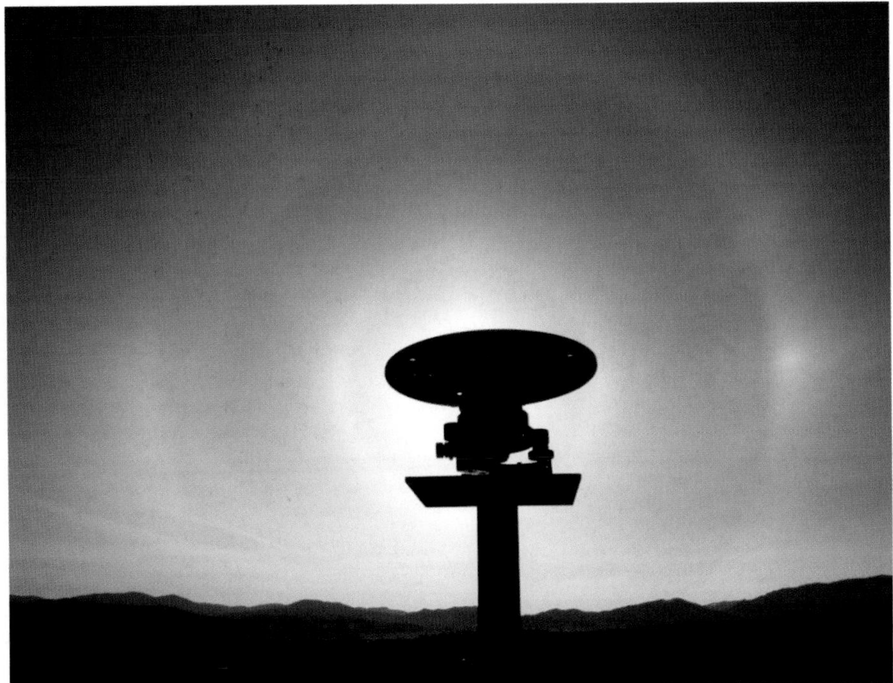

Figure 8.15 Concentric odd-radius halos formed by refraction of sunlight in pyramidal ice crystals (Bozeman, MT, 30 April 2004).

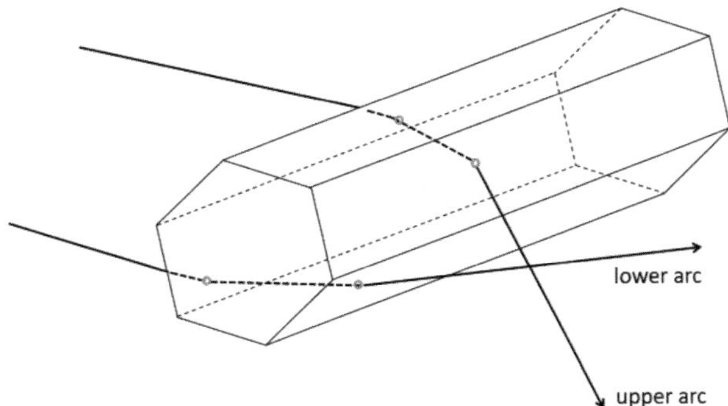

Figure 8.16 Ray paths in hexagonal column crystals that produce the upper and lower tangent arcs and circumscribed halo.

halo whenever enough column crystals fall with their long axis horizontal. (These arcs are sometimes present but always produced when the pencils are horizontal.) These are the upper or lower tangent arcs, formed by light entering one of the six sides of a column crystal and exiting another side angled 60° from the first (Fig. 8.16). The full arc is formed by a collection of horizontally oriented column crystals with random rotation angles in the horizontal plane and about the long axes. The shape of these arcs depend strongly on the sun's elevation angle. Figure 8.17 shows a lower tangent arc at the bottom of a 22° halo.

Figure 8.17 Lower tangent arc below a 22° halo (SEA–BZN, 6 Feb. 2014).

The higher the sun in the sky, the less flared the arcs and the more closely they wrap around the halo top and bottom until they join slightly outside the sides of the 22° halo as a circumscribed halo. This first happens when the sun is about 29° above the horizon. Figure 8.18 shows a circumscribed halo forming an oblate ring outside a 22° halo circle in high, thin cirrus clouds with a sun elevation angle near 50°. At much higher sun angles, the circumscribed halo becomes indistinguishable from a 22° halo.[26] As with all 22° phenomena, the arcs are caused by refraction of light in and out through alternating faces (not adjacent and not opposite).

8.2 Reflections from Ice Crystals

Light also can reflect from ice crystal faces, but it does so with no color dependence, creating a variety of colorless optical effects that can be explained with simple geometric optical ray tracing. The simplest of these effects is a bright reflection of the sun (or moon or other light source) from the tops of horizontally oriented ice crystals. This bright spot is called a subsun (Fig. 8.19) and is an optical effect best seen from the air because you must look down on ice clouds to see it. Figures 8.20 and 8.21 show that the subsun is like a second (weaker) sun, located at an angle below the horizon equal to the sun's angle above the horizon. With horizontally oriented crystals, the subsun is a single bright spot of light; however, as the crystals begin to tilt gently and randomly about the horizontal (Fig. 8.22), the subsun spreads vertically into a subsun pillar—a light pillar extending above or below the subsun (or extending both above and below it).

Figure 8.18 Circumscribed halo and 22° halo (Bozeman, MT, 17 Aug. 2002).

Figure 8.19 Subsun over the Gallatin Mountains (BZN–SLC, 23 March 2004).

Figure 8.20 Subsun located below the horizon by an angle equal to the sun's angle above the horizon, plus a sundog to the right of the sun (BZN–MSP, 6 Feb. 2004).

Light pillars are the ice-crystal equivalents of glitter patterns on water. However, instead of reflections from waves, the pillar is formed by reflections from ice crystals tilted about the horizontal with a random distribution of angles (Fig. 8.22). This display is called a light pillar, or a sun pillar when created by the sun. It is created by reflections from the tops or bottoms of oriented plate crystals, or from the sides of column crystals falling with nearly horizontal long axes.

An observer on the ground will usually see a pillar extending above the rising or setting sun, as in Fig. 8.23. This pillar also has an upper tangent arc flaring out from its top (22° above the sun, where the top of the 22° halo could be). From the air, you can also see a pillar below the sun, a vertically extended subsun called a subsun pillar. Up close, you can see glints from individual ice crystals (Fig. 8.24).

With the sun about 15° above the horizon, you might see what appears to be a pillar below the sun, which is actually a lower tangent arc (Fig. 8.25). Whereas a high sun angle led to the tangent arcs forming a circumscribed halo in Fig. 8.18, a lower sun angle results in the tangent arcs opening up to create V-shaped flares like Fig. 8.23. When the sun is about 15° above the horizon, you cannot see the lower tangent arc from the ground, but you can see it from the air in clouds below the horizon. In that case it resembles a sun pillar at the base of the 22° halo, extending from 7° to about 15° below the horizon (Fig. 8.25). At even lower sun angles, the lower tangent arc again opens into a V shape (Fig. 8.26, this time with a subsun pillar but no 22° halo).

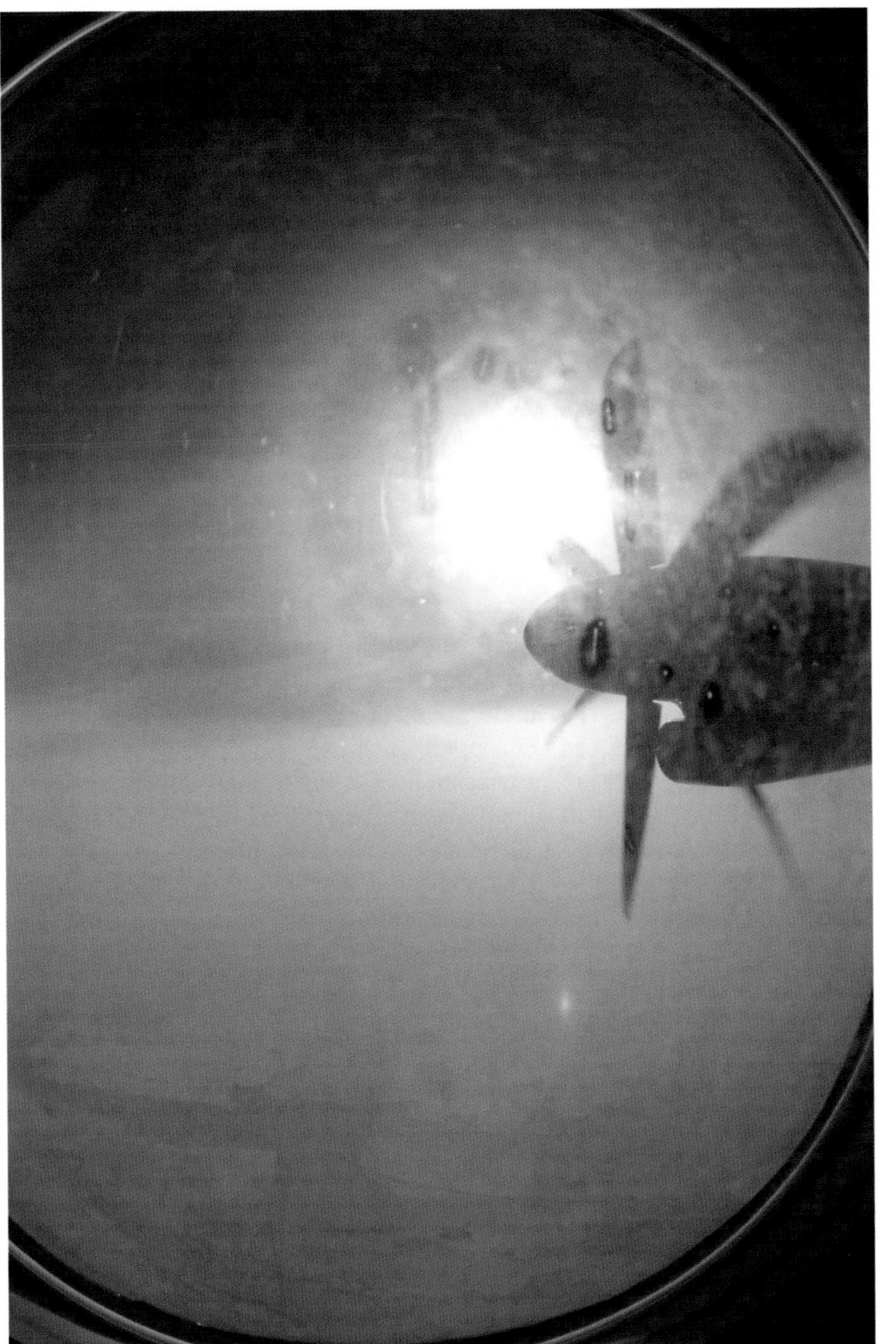

Figure 8.21 A 22° halo with a subsun located below the horizon by an angle equal to the sun's angle above the horizon (SEA–BZN, 6 Feb. 2014).

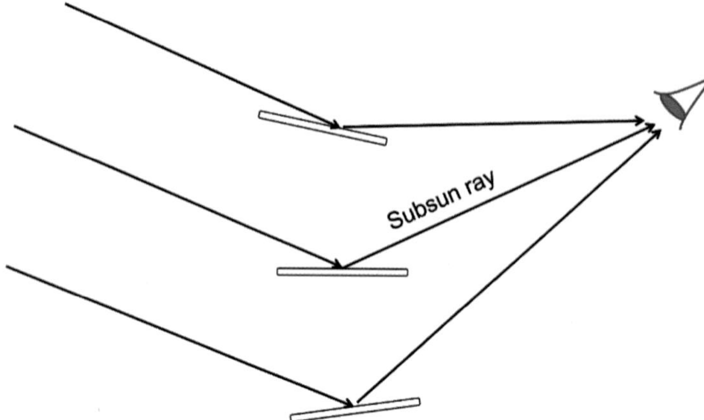

Figure 8.22 Parallel rays from the sun reflect from horizontally oriented ice crystals to create a subsun and from slightly tilted crystals to create a sun pillar that is analogous to a glitter pattern on water (see Section 7.4).

Recall that tangent arcs involve refraction in horizontally oriented column crystals, whereas the 22° halo arises from refraction in hexagonal plate crystals. Therefore, the simultaneous appearance of a tangent arc with a 22° halo implies the presence of both plates and columns (Figs. 8.17 and 8.25).

In cold air, light pillars can sometimes also be seen above unshielded porchlights or street lights (i.e., these pillars are created by light pollution—light that illuminates the sky instead of the porch or street). An airplane equivalent could be a pillar seen above or below a wingtip light while flying through ice crystals). Whereas light from the distant sun arrives at all crystals with the same angle, light from a nearby source arrives at different crystals with different angles that vary with the crystal's location relative to the source, which leads to a much taller pillar for nearby light sources relative to a sun pillar.[27]

8.3 Other Ice Optical Effects

There are numerous different ways that light reflects and refracts from ice in the atmosphere, creating optical effects that range from subtle to stunning. I refer readers interested in learning more about these widely varied optical effects to my colleagues' great books and websites.[1–7] This final section discusses a few ice optical phenomena that are less common than those already mentioned.

8.3.1 Subparhelia

Colored splashes of light located approximately 22° to either side of a subsun are called subparhelia (recall that the formal name for a sundog is parhelion). A subparhelion is a splash of colored light located 22° to the side of the subsun (Fig. 8.27), the same relative geometry as a sundog and sun. It looks like a sundog created by the subsun, but its origin is actually more complicated, involving rays that pass into a plate crystal through a side face, undergo reflection (or an odd

Figure 8.23 Upper tangent arc at the top of a sun pillar at sunset (Bozeman, MT, 7 Dec. 2013).

Figure 8.24 Subsun pillar showing reflections from individual ice crystals (BZN–MSP, 6 Feb. 2004).

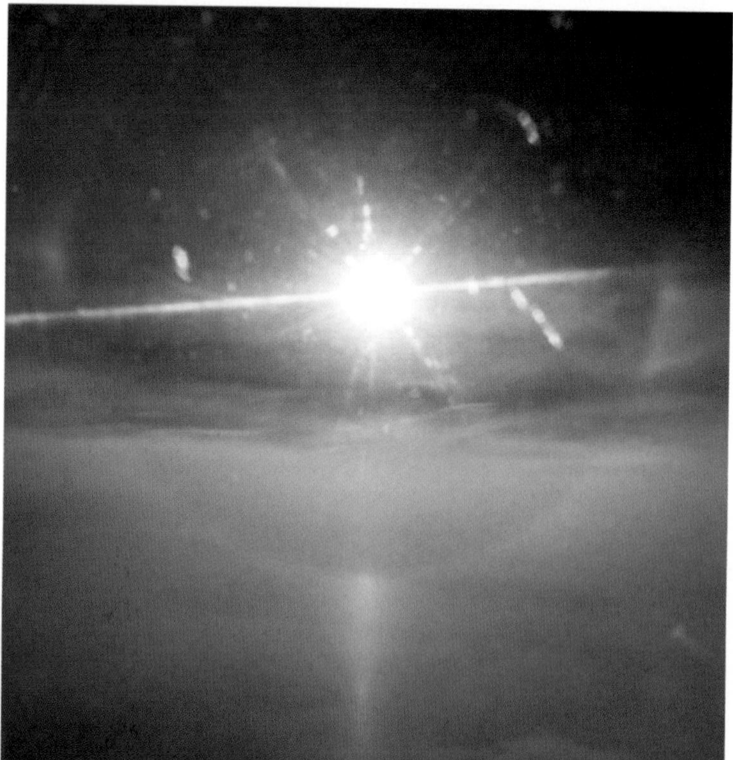

Figure 8.25 Lower tangent arc extending as a vertical flare of light below a 22° halo with a solar elevation angle of 15.6° (MSP–PHX, 2 Aug. 2016).

Figure 8.26 Lower tangent arc and subsun pillar, with a ~7.6° sun elevation angle (JNU–SEA, 30 July 2016). Image reprinted courtesy of Paul Neiman.

Figure 8.27 Subsun and subparhelion (SAN–SLC, 30 Aug. 2007).

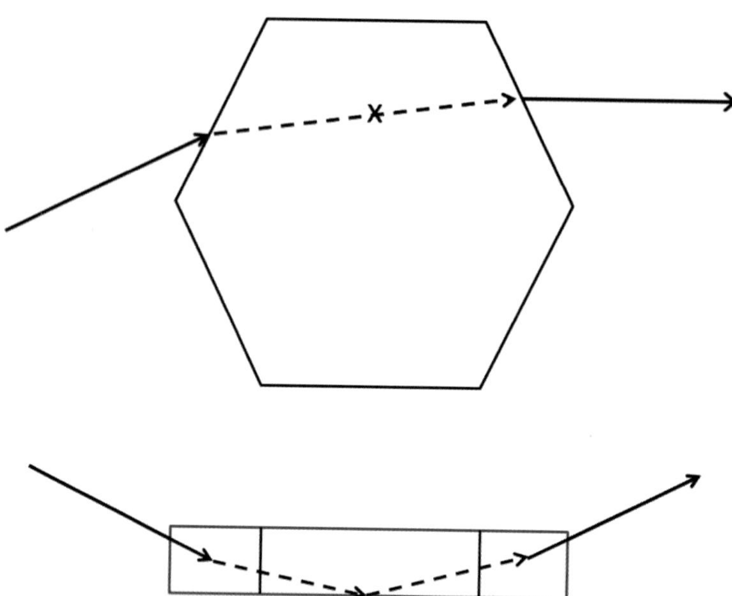

Figure 8.28 Subparhelia are created by rays that are similar to those for normal parhelia (sundogs) but with an odd number of reflections from the bottom surfaces of the plate crystals (this diagram shows one reflection).

number of total internal reflections) from the bottom face, and exit from another vertical side (Fig. 8.28). For parallel bottom and top faces, the exiting ray is directed toward an observer at the same angle as if it were reflected from the top surface of the plate (rays that undergo an even number of internal reflections in this manner add to the parhelia brightness). Therefore, the subparhelion is an optical phenomenon that involves both reflection and refraction in ice crystals.

8.3.2 Refraction in 90° prism ice crystals

Some of the more colorful halo phenomena result from refraction of rays that enter and exit ice crystal faces that form a 90° angle (such as the top and a side face of plate crystals). Such ray paths are like those in a 90° prism, for which the minimum-deviation angle is 46°. Color is more pronounced for these arcs because blue light bends more than red light by approximately 2°, compared to a difference of only 0.75° for the 22° halo. An example is the infralateral arc at the bottom of Fig. 8.29. This colorful arc appears near the location of the very large and rare 46° halo (see Fig. 8.1).[14,15] Therefore, the infralateral arc at the bottom of the photograph is located approximately 24° below the 22° halo seen at the top (i.e., the infralateral arc is located 46° below the sun).

Two additional colorful and easily seen halos generated by 90° prism refractions are the circumhorizontal arc (CHA) and the circumzenithal arc (CZA). Like the 46° halo and related infralateral and supralateral arcs, a CHA is created with 90° prism refractions of light rays that enter vertical sides of horizontally oriented plate crystals and exit the top or bottom faces. Rotations of these crystals about a vertical axis that connects the top and bottom faces produce a circle at constant elevation above the horizon. This colorful arc can extend up to nearly one third of the way around the horizon. Figure 8.30 shows a CHA lying below a 22° halo, near the location where a 46° halo would be if the proper conditions existed. Simulations show that a CHA only touches the 46° halo circle when the sun elevation angle is 68°, and it can only be seen at all when the sun is more than 58° above the horizon.[2] Therefore, a CHA is only visible at lower latitudes, or in the middle latitudes during summer.

A CZA is also a 90° prism refraction phenomenon, but one formed by rays that enter the top or bottom faces of horizontally oriented plate crystals and exit the sides. Again, rotation of the crystals about the vertical axis connecting their top and bottom faces produces a circle at a constant zenith angle. Like a CHA, a CZA has the most vivid colors of refraction halos because it does not suffer from the overlapped colors that occur in 22° halos or sundogs. When the sun is 15° above the horizon, a CZA can cover up to 108° of azimuth angle—nearly a third of the way around the zenith. It also lies very close to the 46° halo circle but is exactly in that location only when the sun is 22° above the horizon. For the CZA to be visible at all, the sun elevation angle must be less than 32°,[2] but it is observed most frequently when the sun is 22° above the horizon.[28] Unfortunately, its position high in the sky makes it difficult to see from an airplane. Although the Internet is loaded with examples of this effect under the name "fire rainbow," it has nothing to do with either fire or a rainbow. Nevertheless, it certainly is beautiful (Fig. 8.31).

Figure 8.29 Infralateral arc below a 22° halo (BZN–MSP, 27 May 2016).

Figure 8.30 Circumhorizontal arc below a 22° halo (Bozeman, MT, 20 June 2015).

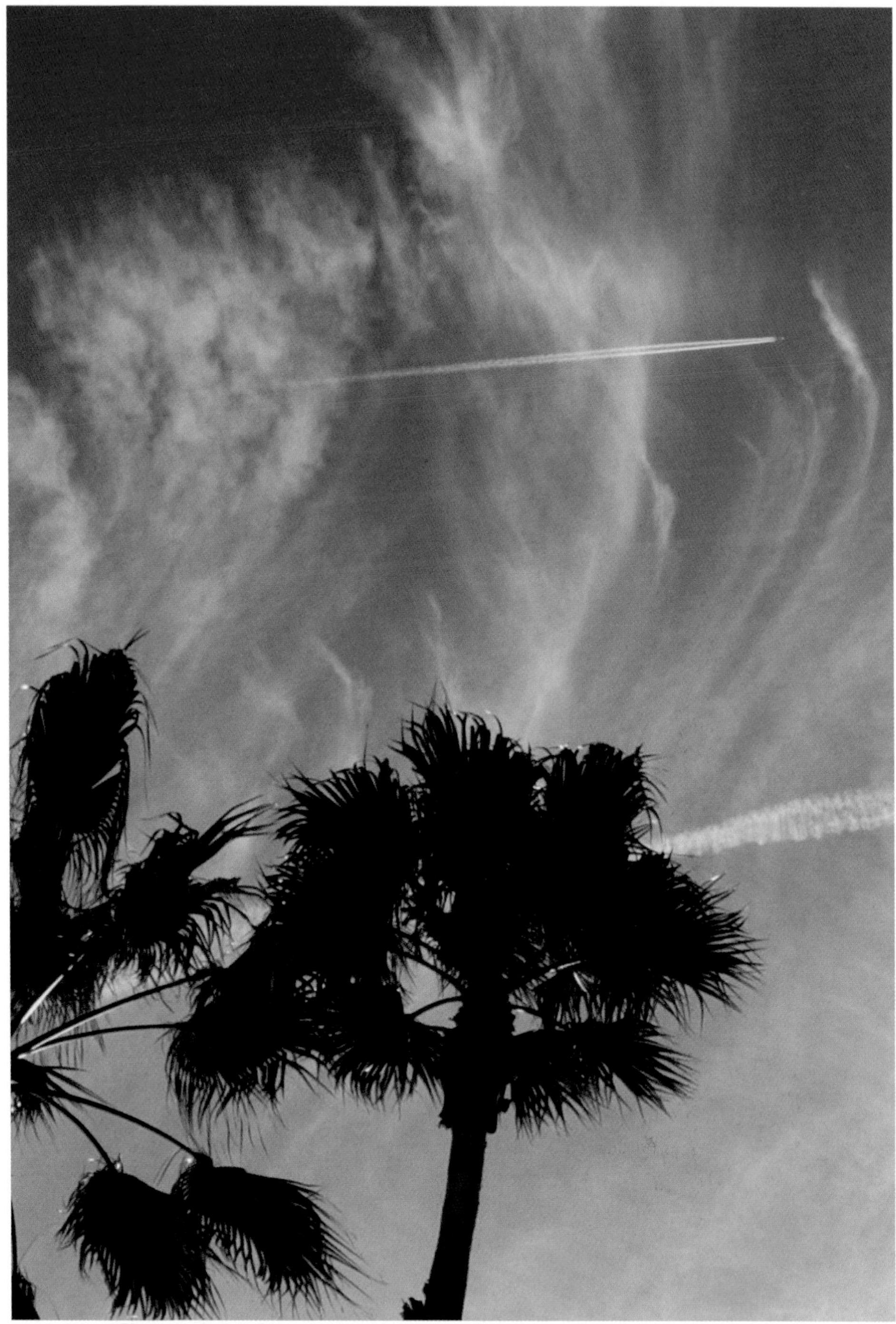

Figure 8.31 Circumzenithal arc (Orlando, FL, 20 March 2008).

8.3.3 Bottlinger's rings

The final halo discussed here is called Bottlinger's rings: a small elliptical halo that is seen very rarely surrounding the subsun. The cause of this rare halo effect is not understood yet, although there are discussions in the literature of potential mechanisms involving refraction in crystals with weakly sloped ends or multi-branched dendrite shapes.[29,30]

Figure 8.32 is a rare photograph of Bottlinger's rings. I took this photograph on a morning flight from my home town of Bozeman, MT to Salt Lake City, UT, just after the airplane passed over the Wasatch Mountains and began to descend into the Salt Lake Valley. The air temperature at the halo altitude was near –15 °C. Note that it is important to distinguish between Bottlinger's rings, which are elliptical but centered on the subsun, from the more general elliptical halos, which are centered on the sun itself (small elliptical halos have been observed with semi-major angular widths of 2.8–6.0° and semi-minor angular widths of 1.5–5.6°).[30,31] I hope that the inclusion of this rare halo photograph motivates you to watch not only for the common halos but also the less frequent ones, some of which are not fully explained.

Figure 8.32 Rare appearance of Bottlinger's rings, a mysterious elliptical halo surrounding the subsun (BZN–SLC, 5 Nov. 2013).

References

1. R. G. Greenler, *Rainbows, Halos, and Glories*, Elton-Wolf Publishing, Milwaukee, WI (2000).
2. W. Tape, *Atmospheric Halos*, Am. Geophys. Union, Washington, D.C. (1994).
3. W. Tape, *Atmospheric Halos and the Search for Angle X*, Am. Geophysical Union, Washington, D.C. (2006).
4. D. Lynch and W. Livingston, *Color and Light in Nature*, 3rd ed., Thule Scientific, Topanga, CA (2010).
5. D. Lynch, "Atmospheric halos," *Sci. Am.* **238**(4), 144–152 (1978).
6. http://www.atoptics.co.uk/halosim.htm.
7. S. R. Wilk, "Every dog has his day," *Weatherwise* **55**(6), 34–37 (2002).
8. U. Nakaya, *Snow Crystals: Natural and Artificial*, Harvard University Press, Cambridge, MA (1954).
9. W. A. Bentley and W. J. Humphreys, *Snow Crystals*, Dover Publications, New York (1962).
10. K. G. Libbrecht and R. Wing, *The Snowflake: Winter's Frozen Artistry*, Voyageur Press, Minneapolis, MN (2015).
11. K. G. Libbrecht, "The physics of snow crystals," *Rep. Prog. Phys*. **68**(4), 855–895 (2005).
12. W. Tape, "Some ice crystals that made halos," *J. Opt. Soc. Am.* **73**(12), 1641–1645 (1983).
13. K. Sassen, N. C. Knight, Y. Takano, and A. J. Heymsfield, "Effects of ice crystal structure on halo formation: Cirrus cloud experimental and ray-tracing modeling studies," *Appl. Opt.* **33**(21), 4500–4600 (1994).
14. K. Sassen, "Halos in cirrus clouds: Why are classic displays so rare?" *Appl. Opt*. **44**(27), 5684–5687 (2005).
15. M. Vollmer and J. A. Shaw, "Brilliant colours from a white snow cover," *Phys. Ed.* **48**(3), 322-331 (2013).
16. S. D. Gedzelman, "Approach to photorealistic halo simulations," *Appl. Opt.* **50**(28), F102–F111 (2011).
17. S. D. Gedzelman, "Simulating halos and coronas in their atmospheric environment," *Appl. Opt.* **47**(34), H157–H166 (2008).
18. S. D. Gedzelman and M. Vollmer, "Atmospheric optical phenomena and radiative transfer," *Bull. Am. Meteorol. Soc*. **89**(4), 471–485 (2008).
19. E. Tränkle and R. G. Greenler, "Multiple-scattering effects in halo phenomena," *J. Opt. Soc. Am. A* **4**(3), 591–599 (1987).
20. G. P. Können, "Polarization and intensity distributions of refraction halos," *J. Opt. Soc. Am.* **73**(12), 1629–1639 (1983).

21. G. P. Können, *Polarized Light in Nature*, Cambridge University Press, Cambridge (1985).
22. G. P. Können, "Identification of odd-radius halo arcs and of 44°/46° parhelia by their inner-edge polarization," *Appl. Opt.* **37**(9), 1450–1456 (1998).
23. G. P. Können, H. R. A. Wessels, and J. Tinbergen, "Halo polarization profiles and sampled ice crystals: observations and interpretation," *Appl. Opt.* **42**(3), 309–317 (2003).
24. P. J. Neiman, "The Boulder, Colorado, concentric halo display of 21 July 1986," *Bull. Am. Meteorol. Soc.* **70**(3), 258–264 (1989).
25. M. Pekkola, M. Riikonen, J. Moilanen, and J. Ruoskanen, "Halo arcs from airborne, pyramidal ice crystals falling with their c axes in vertical orientation," *Appl. Opt.* **37**(9), 1434–1440 (1998).
26. http://www.atoptics.co.uk/halo/circsalt.htm
27. A. J. Mallmann, J. L. Hock, and R. G. Greenler, "Comparison of Sun pillars with light pillars from nearby light sources," *Appl. Opt.* **37**(9), 1441–1449 (1998).
28. R. S. McDowell, "Frequency analysis of the circumzenithal arc: Evidence for the oscillation of ice-crystal plates in the upper atmosphere," *J. Opt. Soc. Am.* **69**(8), 1119–1122 (1979).
29. D. K. Lynch, S. D. Gedzelman, and A. B. Fraser, "Subsuns, Bottlinger's rings, and elliptical halos," *Appl. Opt.* **33**(21), 4580–4589 (1994).
30. E. Tränkle and M. Riikonen, "Elliptical halos, Bottlinger's rings, and the ice-plate snow-star transition," *Appl. Opt.* **33**(21), 4871–4878 (1994).
31. M. Riikonen and J. Ruoskanen, "Observations of vertically elliptical halos," *Appl. Opt.* **33**(21), 4537–4538 (1994).

Chapter 9
Noctilucent Clouds and Aurora

Flying at high latitudes provides a unique opportunity for spectacular scenery and at least three unique optical phenomena: extremes in the length of day or night; wispy, noctilucent clouds at the edge of space; and swirling, colorful aurora. These occurrences appear not only during flights to or from the far north or south but also on flights along great circle routes that swing temporarily far north or south. You can enhance your time in high-latitude regions by selecting flights between higher-latitude cities. For example, when flying to Europe I like to connect in a northern city, such as Amsterdam.

9.1 Midnight Sun

Some of my favorite memories from growing up in Alaska are connected with the great community celebrations on the summer solstice when the sky was light all night long. Where I lived, the sun actually did set for a few hours that night, but it never went very far below the horizon. Therefore, the summertime sky never got very dark until August, and the wintertime sky never got very bright until late February. This was just south of the Arctic Circle, but locations north of the Arctic Circle experience the true midnight sun, circling overhead all day long and moving toward the horizon at night without ever reaching it.

Figure 9.1 is a photograph of the sun at midnight in mid-July in Barrow, AK (latitude 71.3°N). Conversely, Fig. 9.2 shows how dark the subarctic sky is during a midwinter afternoon over Iceland. The dot of light above the wing on the right side of the picture is the planet Jupiter, which I watched appear and disappear as the plane flew into and out of the subarctic twilight.

9.2 Noctilucent Clouds

Have you ever seen sunlit clouds in the dark night sky? Noctilucent, or "night-shining," clouds can be lit by the sun an hour or two after sunset or before sunrise (Fig. 9.3) because of their extraordinarily high altitude: near 85 km, literally at the edge of space (Fig. 9.4).[1] When you fly at an altitude near 10 km, all but the highest cirrus clouds lie below you. Even the few higher clouds are only a few kilometers above your airplane. All of these clouds and the weather systems they accompany reside within the lowest layer of the atmosphere, called the troposphere, more than five times lower than noctilucent clouds (NLCs).

Figure 9.1 Midnight-sun glitter on the Arctic Ocean (Barrow, AK, 12 July 2012).

Figure 9.2 The high-latitude sky can be quite dark during "day" in the winter, as shown in this photograph of Iceland on a winter afternoon, and quite bright during "night" in the summer (AMS–MSP, 11 Jan. 2014).

Figure 9.3 Noctilucent clouds at 04:36 am (1.5 h before sunrise) during nautical twilight, with the sun 10.9° below the horizon (Bozeman, MT, 16 July 2009).

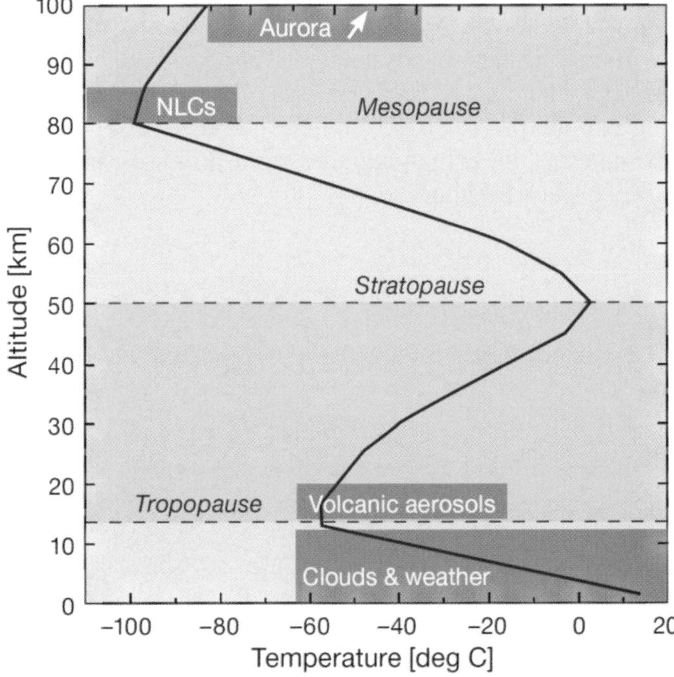

Figure 9.4 Noctilucent clouds form at the edge of space, near an 80-km altitude.[1]

These clouds form so high in the atmosphere that they are lit by the sun when normal clouds and the vast majority of the atmosphere lie in darkness about an hour or two after sunset or before sunrise (Fig. 9.5).[1] They are so optically thin that their scattered light is only visible against the dark twilight sky.[1,2] The best viewing time is when the sun is approximately 9–12° below the horizon, but visibility might be possible for solar depression angles from 6–15°, through nautical twilight and into the beginning of astronomical twilight. With a higher sun, atmospheric scattering overwhelms the light from these ultrathin clouds. With a lower sun, these near-space clouds disappear into the shadow of night.

The proper conditions for noctilucent cloud formation exist only during summer, when the temperature at 80 km falls to –100 °C or even colder.[2] This occurs only at latitudes above 50°, and for much of the summer the sky is too bright at latitudes above about 60°, so noctilucent clouds are most readily observed in a narrow band between 50–60° latitude. For reference, Calgary, Canada and London, UK are both at about 51°N, whereas Anchorage, AK is near 61°N and Helsinki, Finland is near 60°N.

In recent years there have been increased reports of noctilucent clouds seen from lower latitudes.[1–3] This may be a result of greenhouse gases that warm the troposphere and cool the mesosphere,[4] but it may also be related to improved awareness and expanded Internet-based reporting opportunities.

An example of a rare midlatitude display of noctilucent clouds appears in Fig. 9.3, which was photographed in Bozeman, MT at 45.65°N latitude on 16 July 2009. I could see faint NLCs on the two previous nights, so I got up very early and went outside to watch the sky. At 4:28 am MDT (UTC-6 h), 1.5 h before sunrise, the delicate swirls and feathery bands in Fig. 9.3 appeared rather suddenly, literally out of the darkness. The display persisted while the sun was 11.8–7.7° below the horizon, fading into the pre-dawn sky an hour before sunrise. At lower latitudes, NLCs can fade quickly, but at high latitudes the nearly horizontal path of the sun makes these displays last for hours.

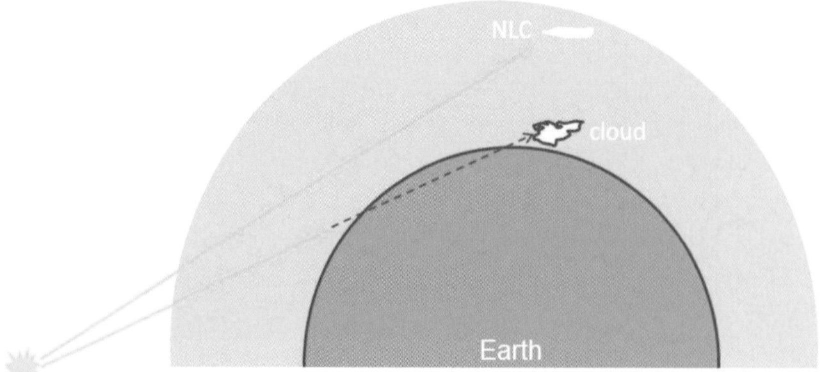

Figure 9.5 Noctilucent clouds are so high that they are illuminated by the sun when normal clouds and the rest of the atmosphere are in darkness.[1]

Noctilucent clouds are made of water ice crystals that have nucleated on submicrometer particles of meteoric dust (e.g., iron and nickel). These ice crystals scatter light with very little color dependence. Absorption of violet and yellow-red light by ozone in the stratosphere results in ghost-like, silvery-blue clouds that often exhibit complex patterns of waves and swirls (Fig. 9.6).[1–3,5]

Your best chance of seeing NLCs from the air is on a high-latitude, nighttime flight in June, July, or August in the northern hemisphere (December–February in the southern hemisphere). Sit on the side of the plane that affords the best view of the northern sky (southern sky in the southern hemisphere) and pay closest attention when your airplane is above latitude 50°. You can monitor online forums for NLC activity before and even during your flight.

The night after I took the photograph in Fig. 9.6, I saw more NLCs during an overnight flight from Alaska. About an hour after leaving Fairbanks at sunset, we broke through the clouds near Skagway, AK, and NLCs began appearing to our east (Fig. 9.7). This display brightened as we flew into a darker sky and remained visible for 1.5 h. The peak display (Fig. 9.8) occurred when we were south of Fort Liard, NWT, Canada at latitude ~59.6°N. I explained to people around me what we were seeing, but most of them fell asleep before it got even better.

Figure 9.6 Noctilucent clouds covering a large portion of the late-summertime Alaskan sky (Fairbanks, AK; 7 Aug. 2013).

Figure 9.7 Noctilucent clouds just becoming visible in deep twilight (FAI–MSP, 8 Aug. 2013).

Figure 9.8 Noctilucent clouds shining in the deep subarctic twilight (FAI–MSP, 8 Aug. 2013).

9.3 Aurora

As the twilight sky on my Fairbanks–Minneapolis flight grew darker, a band of green aurora became visible above the NLCs I had been watching (Fig. 9.9). These two high-latitude optical phenomena could be seen together for about a half hour, but passable photographs were only possible for a few minutes because of how much brighter the NLCs were than the aurora. The aurora remained visible for a full hour and peaked when we were northwest of Fort McMurray, AB, Canada at latitude 57.4°N (Fig. 9.10).

An aurora is an optical phenomenon that results from energetic particles from the sun being captured by the earth's magnetic field and colliding with atoms and molecules of gas in the very highest reaches of our atmosphere between approximately 100–400 km, even higher than NLCs.[6–10] The collisions release energy in the form of visible light, with colors determined by the energy levels in the emitting gas molecules or atoms. The most common aurora color is green, with a wavelength of 557.7 nm, as seen in Figs. 9.9 and 9.10 and most of the subsequent aurora photographs in this chapter (Figs. 9.11–9.14). This ubiquitous green light is emitted by oxygen atoms. Additional colors that are sometimes visible include a purplish combination of red and blue from nitrogen, usually at the bottom of an auroral arc (Figs. 9.11–9.13) and deep red from oxygen, usually at the top of an arc (Fig. 9.15).

Figure 9.9 Rare photograph of noctilucent clouds and aurora together (FAI–MSP, 8 Aug. 2013).

Figure 9.10 Bright green aurora with deep twilight colors (FAI–MSP, 8 Aug. 2013).

Figure 9.11 Purple and green aurora with arctic twilight colors (MSP–AMS, 22 June 2015).

Figure 9.12 Purple and green aurora fading into a brightening sky (MSP–AMS, 22 June 2015).

Like NLCs, an aurora is a high-latitude optical phenomenon. You are most likely to see it within a region called the auroral oval. The oval is centered on the geomagnetic north pole and expands southward with increasing solar storms (northward in the southern hemisphere). The best latitudes for seeing the aurora are near 65°, which is the approximate latitude of Fairbanks, AK, Reykjavik, Iceland, and Oulu, Finland. However, an aurora can also be seen in the middle latitudes during energetic solar storms.[10] There are multiple Internet sites where you can monitor the auroral oval in real time[11–13] or explore an aurora forecast[14] to assess your chances of seeing it on an upcoming flight.

Auroras are driven by solar activity, which increases and decreases on an approximately eleven-year cycle. Flying through a high-latitude region near the peak of this cycle ("solar maximum") can increase your chances of seeing an aurora, but I have seen many excellent auroras near solar minimum. There is also a moderate seasonal dependence, with peaks near the spring and fall equinoxes; however, I took the photographs in Figs. 9.11–9.13 on a trans-Atlantic flight during the summer solstice—the shortest and brightest high-latitude night of the year. The key is being in the right place at just the right time, which happened ironically for me on this occasion because a delay caused me to miss my planned flight and instead take the one I originally wanted but could not afford. I am very grateful to the kind person who traded their window seat for my aisle seat on what became one of my best aurora-viewing flights ever! On this midsummer flight, the sky never got fully dark, but I still had great views of multi-colored aurora for about two hours while we crossed the northeastern edge of Canada and passed south of Greenland (Figs. 9.11–9.13).

Figure 9.13 Final view of purple and green aurora before sunrise (MSP–AMS, 22 June 2015).

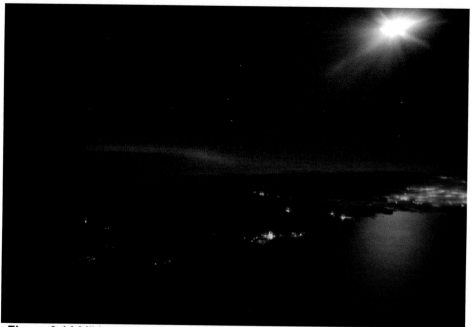

Figure 9.14 Mild green aurora arc with a rising moon (ANC–SEA, 2 Oct. 2015).

On most high-latitude flights, you are most likely to see a relatively stationary green aurora arc like the one in Fig. 9.14. However, you might sometimes see more dynamic and colorful ones, such as those in Figs. 9.10–9.13. It is really quite a different experience watching a dynamic aurora through a small airplane window than from the ground where you can see the full sky, unobscured, as in the all-sky photograph of Fig. 9.15. However, it can also be breathtaking because of how your position in the air somehow adds to the sensation of aurora colors floating high in space.

The hardest part of observing auroras from an airplane is shielding your view of the dark sky from reflections of the numerous interior lights. I cover my head with a coat or a doubled-up airplane blanket and use my arms to seal the coat or blanket against the window to block the interior light as effectively as possible. I usually shoot photographs with a handheld camera because it is pointless to mount the camera to a tripod that is sitting on the continually rolling airplane. This setup only works successfully with a high camera ISO setting, an optically fast lens, and good technique that relies on a very steady set of hands.

Figure 9.15 All-sky photograph of an aurora, with north at the top and east to the left (Poker Flat Research Range near Fairbanks, AK, 11 April 2016).

Figure 9.16 Red aurora from oxygen emission (Bozeman, MT, 8 Nov. 2004).

The chapter closes with a nearly pure red aurora (Fig. 9.16), caused by red oxygen emission. This is a relatively rare red aurora that I have yet to capture from the air, so I show this photograph taken in my back yard to encourage all of us to watch for an opportunity to photograph a similar display from an airplane. This photograph also illustrates what great auroras can be seen occasionally from midlatitude locations.

References

1. J. A. Shaw, "Night-shining clouds," *Opt. Photon. News* **21**(6), 20–25 (2010).
2. A. Dubietis et al., "Noctilucent clouds: modern ground-based photographic observations by a digital camera network," *Appl. Opt.* **50**(28), F72–F79 (2011).
3. V. B. Wickwar, M. J. Taylor, and J. P. Herron, "Visual and lidar observations of noctilucent clouds above Logan, Utah, at 41.7°N," *J. Geophys. Res.* **107**(D7), 4054 (2002).
4. G. E. Thomas and J. Olivero, "Noctilucent clouds as possible indicators of global change in the mesosphere," *Adv. Space Res.* **28**(7), 937–946 (2001).

5. R. L. Collins, M. C. Kelley, M. J. Nicolls, C. Ramos, T. Hou, T. E. Stern, K. Mizutani, and T. Itabe, "Simultaneous lidar observations of a noctilucent cloud and an internal wave in the polar mesosphere," *J. Geophys. Res.* **108**, 8435 (2003).
6. S.-I. Akasofu, J. Finch, and T. Brown, *The Northern Lights: Secrets of the Aurora Borealis,* Alaska Northwest Books, Portland, OR (2009).
7. S.-I. Akasofu, "Why do auroras look the way they do?" *EOS* **80**(17), 193, 198–199 (1999).
8. S.-I. Akasofu, "The dynamic aurora," *Sci. Am.*, **260**(5), 90–97 (1989).
9. N. Davis, *Aurora Watcher's Handbook*, University of Alaska Press, Fairbanks, AK (1992).
10. J. A. Shaw, "What we see in the aurora," *Opt. Photon. News* **10**(11), 20–24 (1999).
11. www.aurorasaurus.org
12. www.swpc.noaa.gov
13. www.spaceweather.com
14. www.gi.alaska.edu/auroraforecast

Chapter 10
Colors from Polarization

10.1 Skylight Polarization

The same scattering process that creates sky colors also alters the skylight polarization, which is the tendency for the electric field associated with the light to oscillate preferentially in a particular direction. Sunlight is randomly polarized, with no preferred orientation for its electric field. This light becomes partially polarized when it is scattered by atmospheric gas molecules or aerosols. In fact, an ideal Rayleigh scattering event creates perfectly polarized light 90° from the sun. However, gas molecules are not ideal Rayleigh particles, and the light undergoes multiple scattering events, so there is a band of highly, but not perfectly, polarized light stretching across the clear sky, 90° from the sun.

A measurement of the sky polarization pattern is shown in Fig. 10.1 at a 670-nm wavelength for a clear sky. This all-sky image was recorded by an instrument we designed and built at Montana State University in Bozeman, MT.[1] The outer circle is the horizon, the center is the zenith, and the colors at the right of the image denote the degree of polarization, ranging from 0 to 1 (0% for random polarization to 100% for total linear polarization). The yellow region is the band of maximum polarization, located 90° from the sun (hidden behind the occulter at the lower left). If you wore polarized sunglasses and rocked your head back and forth while looking at the highly polarized part of the sky, you would see the sky alternating between bright and dark. But it would never go completely dark, as it would if it was 100% polarized. Throughout the day the band of maximum polarization moves across the sky, always oriented 90° from the sun. Its maximum value changes with aerosols and surface reflectance.[1–6] The obstructions near the top of this image are a large radio antenna and two penthouses on the roof of the building where the all-sky imager was mounted.

10.2 Colors from Birefringent Airplane Windows

Beautiful pastel colors can be seen by sandwiching a transparent birefringent material between two polarizing filters with orthogonal transmission axes (i.e., "crossed polarizers"). Partially polarized skylight can serve as the first of these polarizers. For example, Fig. 1.4 shows colors that appeared when I took a picture of skylight through the birefringent window with a polarizing filter on my camera.

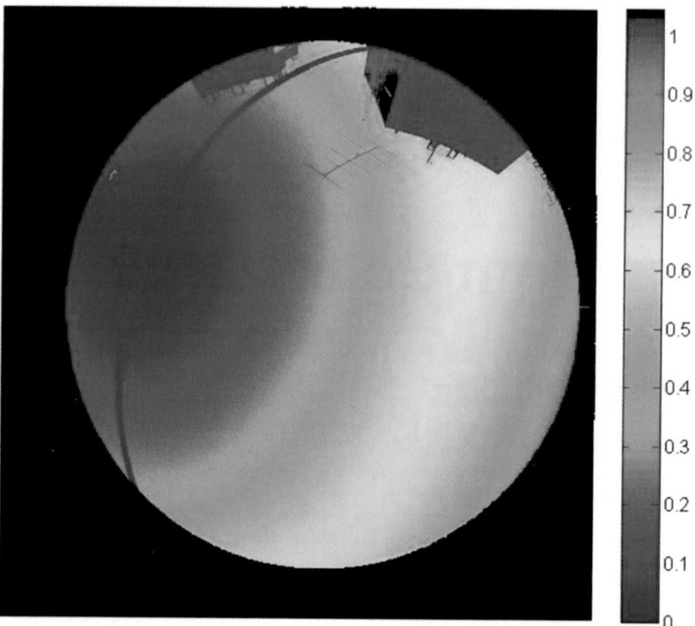

Figure 10.1 All-sky image of the degree of polarization in a clear sky (Bozeman, MT, 23 Feb. 2016, 13:33:30 Mountain Standard Time = UTC-7 hours)[1–4]

However, similar colors can be seen without using a polarizing filter on the lens if the light coming through the window undergoes an additional polarization-altering reflection or transmission. In fact, some modest birefringence colors can be seen even without a polarizer if the light passes through a birefringent material at moderately large angles.[7]

An example of this scenario is light passing obliquely through an airplane window (Fig. 10.2). In this case, the beam of light coming through the window suggests that the source is direct sunlight, not diffusely scattered skylight. It appears that in this case randomly polarized sunlight became partially polarized on transmission through the outer surface of the window, then this partially polarized light generated pastel colors because of the wavelength-dependent transmission through the additional birefringent window material. Figure 10.3 shows another example of pastel colors that were visible by eye when looking through the window at a large incidence angle.

Figure 10.4 is an example of pastel colors made visible with a polarizing filter on my camera lens, rotated to achieve maximum effect. The colors appear most vividly in the part of the scene where the skylight is most strongly polarized. In this case, there is very little pastel coloration in the bottom half of the image because the sky is less polarized there (recall Fig. 2.1) and also because of lower contrast in that part of the scene. Here and in general, the colors tend to be green, yellow-green, and purple (red with blue) because of the wavelength dependence of the polarizer and retarder transmission, as well as the blue spectrum of skylight.[8,9]

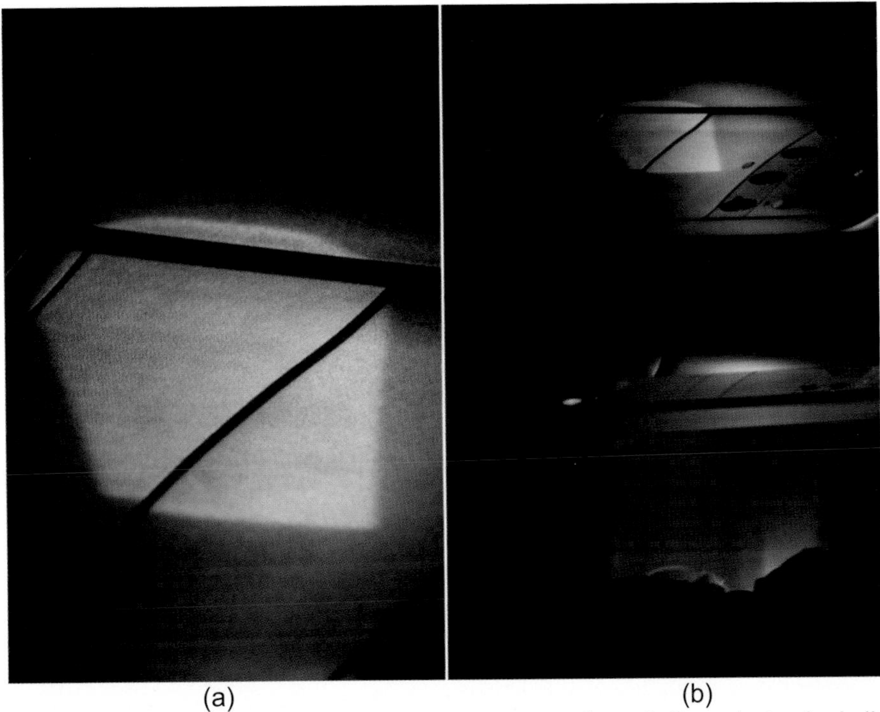

(a) (b)

Figure 10.2 Colors resulting from the passage of partially polarized skylight through a birefringent airplane window: (a) close-up view without a polarizer and (b) wider view for context (AMS–MSP, 6 June 2010, near Iceland).

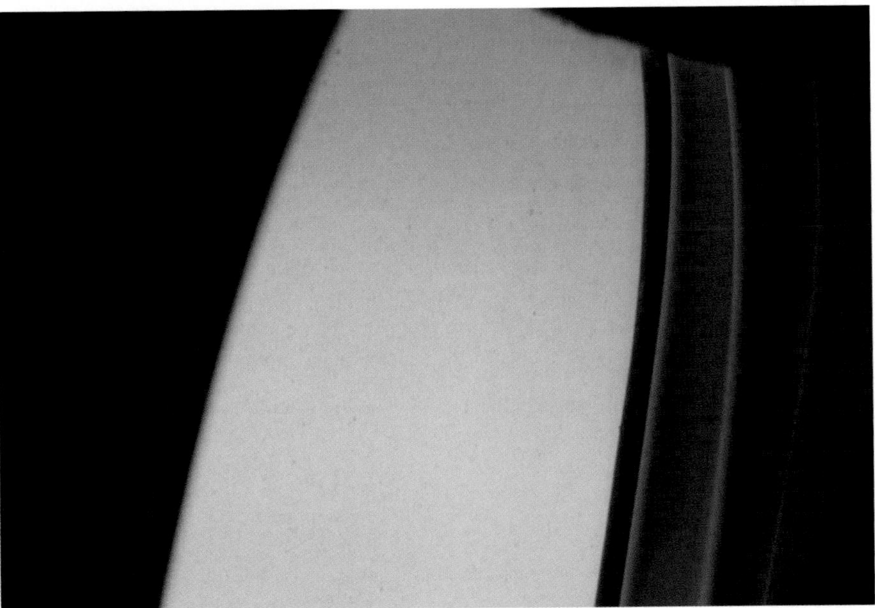

Figure 10.3 Pastel colors seen at a large incidence angle through a birefringent airplane window without a polarizer (MSP– or SLC–MCO, 27 April 2011).

Figure 10.4 Colors arising from viewing partially polarized skylight through a birefringent airplane window with a polarizing filter on the camera lens (SLC–SEA, 17 June 2010).

The final example, Fig. 10.5, is a photograph of the Eiffel Tower I took from a subway car during the few seconds it traversed a bridge over the River Seine in Paris, France. As the car emerged from underground, I realized that I still had a polarizing filter on my lens and with no time to remove it, I quickly rotated it for "best effect" and was delighted with the result.

A slightly more advanced explanation of why we see these colors is that the window acts like a retarder with a wavelength-dependent transmission.[8,9] The birefringent retarder has a "fast" axis for a particular polarization orientation and a "slow" axis for the orthogonal polarization). The first polarizer generates polarized light at some angle from the axis of the retarder. The result is that two components of the incident light, one parallel to the fast axis and the other perpendicular, undergo different phase delays in passing through the birefringent window. These phase delays depend on wavelength. When the elliptically polarized light emerging from the window encounters the second polarizer, only certain colors have the proper phase shift to be polarized such that they can pass through the second polarizer. Therefore, the light we see has colored patterns that relate to the spatial pattern of birefringence in the window.

Figure 10.5 The Eiffel Tower with pastel colors arising from photographing polarized skylight through a birefringent subway-car window with a polarizing filter on the camera lens (Paris, 5 July 2015).

References

1. N. J. Pust and J. A. Shaw, "Dual-field imaging polarimeter using liquid crystal variable retarders," *Appl. Opt.* **45**(22), 5470–5478 (2006).
2. N. J. Pust and J. A. Shaw, "Digital all-sky polarization imaging of partly cloudy skies," *Appl. Opt.* **47**(34), H190–H198 (2008).
3. A. R. Dahlberg, N. J. Pust, and J. A. Shaw, "Effects of surface reflectance on skylight polarization measurements at the Mauna Loa Observatory," *Opt. Express* **19**(17), 16008–16021 (2011.
4. N. J. Pust and J. A. Shaw, "Wavelength dependence of the degree of polarization in cloud-free skies: simulations of real environments," *Opt. Express* **20**(14), 15559–15568 (2012).
5. K. L. Coulson, *Polarization and Intensity of Light in the Atmosphere*, A. Deepak Publishing, Hampton, VA (1988).
6. G. P. Können, *Polarized Light in Nature*, Cambridge University Press, Cambridge (1985).
7. Y. Zhang, L. Chen, S. Wang, and H. Zhou, "Formation of birefringence patterns under everyday conditions," *Eur. J. Phys.* **35**, 055008 (2014).
8. C. F. Bohren, "On the gamut of colors seen through birefringent airplane windows," *Appl. Opt.* **30**(24), 3474–3478 (1991).
9. C. F. Bohren, "Window watching and polarized light," *Weatherwise* **41**(2), 105–110 (1988).

Chapter 11
Scenery and Interesting Sights

In addition to the optical phenomena that are the primary focus of this book, there are many interesting scenes and sights to see out your airplane window. Most of them include some aspect of the concepts discussed here. The following is a brief sampling of some of my favorites.

Figure 11.1 Bridger Mountains: the mountains I see each time I leave or return home (SLC–BZN, 21 June 2006).

Figure 11.2 Teton Mountains on the Idaho–Wyoming border (SLC–BZN, 18 Nov. 2006).

Figure 11.3 Mt. Rainier peeking between cloud layers (SEA–SLC, 18 Nov. 2015).

Figure 11.4 Snow-covered Mt. Fuji rising above the clouds (HND–KOJ, 25 March 2016).

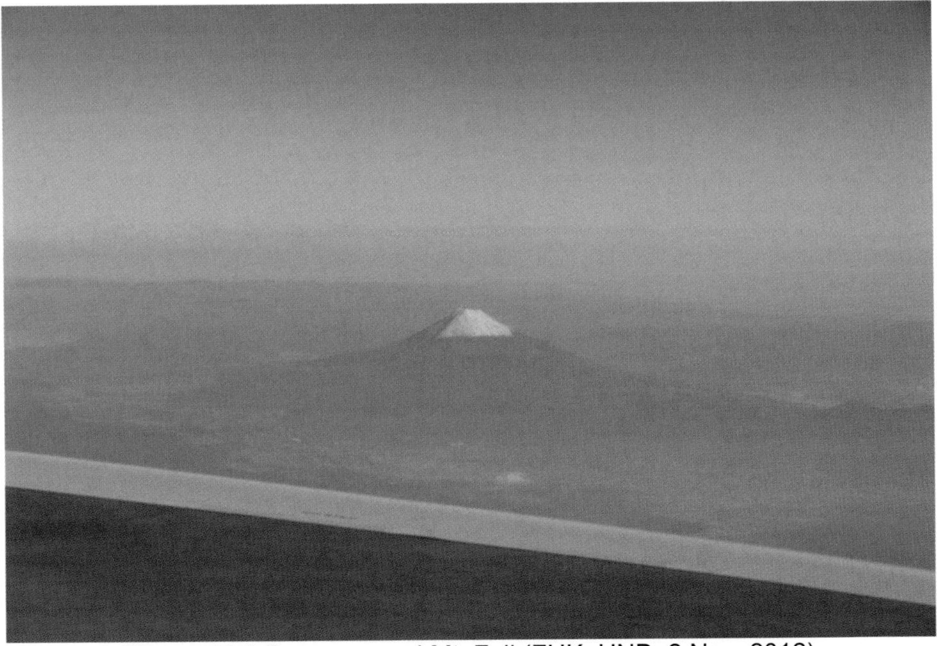

Figure 11.5 Snow-capped Mt. Fuji (FUK–HND, 2 Nov. 2012).

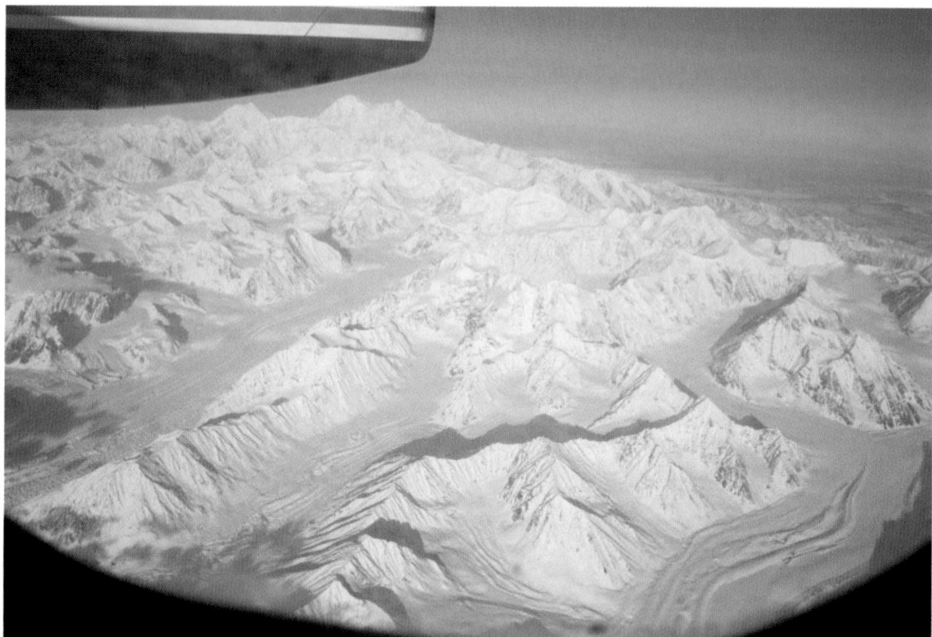

Figure 11.6 Denali, the tallest mountain in North America (FAI–ANC, 15 April 2016).

Figure 11.7 Denali seen up close when the Alaska Air pilot gave us a special "mountain tour" (FAI–ANC, 29 July 2014).

Figure 11.8 The Lincoln Memorial and Washington Monument at night (MSP–DCA, 15 June 2010).

Figure 11.9 The Lincoln Memorial and Washington Monument in daylight (DCA–SLC, 2 May 2013).

Figure 11.10 San Francisco, CA and the Golden Gate Bridge (SFO–SLC, 17 Dec. 2008).

Figure 11.11 Coronado Island and San Diego, CA (SAN–SLC, 20 Aug. 2014).

Figure 11.12 Los Angeles, CA (SLC–LAX, 12 Nov. 2014).

Figure 11.13 Mexico City, Mexico (MEX–ATL, 15 Nov. 2014).

Figure 11.14 Condensation "shadows" of airplanes previously parked at Albuquerque, New Mexico (ABQ–SLC, 11 Feb. 2010).

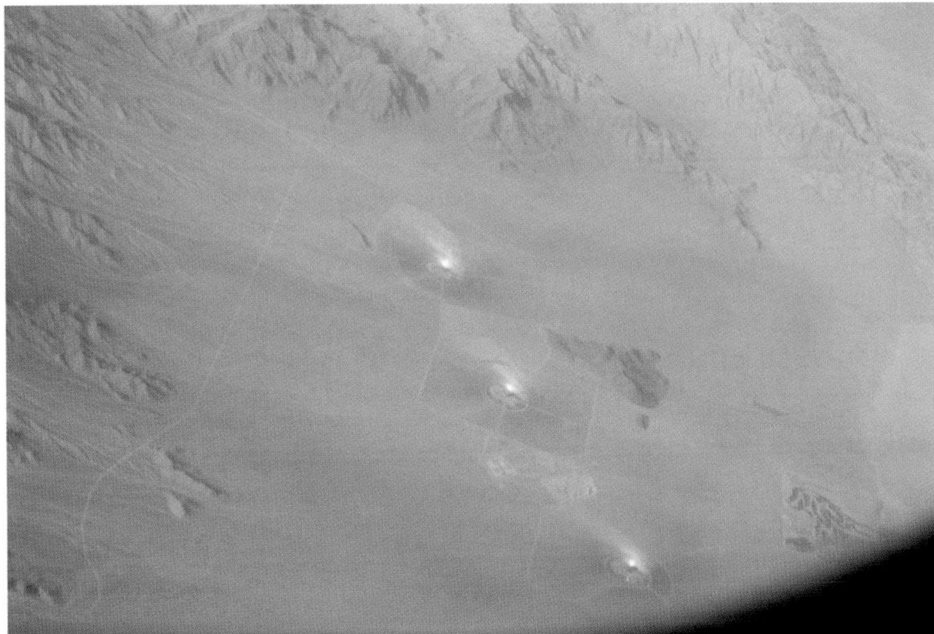

Figure 11.15 Solar concentrators in the California desert (SLC–LAX, 12 Nov. 2014).

Figure 11.16 Fractal coastline of Lake Mead at the Nevada–Arizona border (SLC–SAN, 20 Aug. 2011).

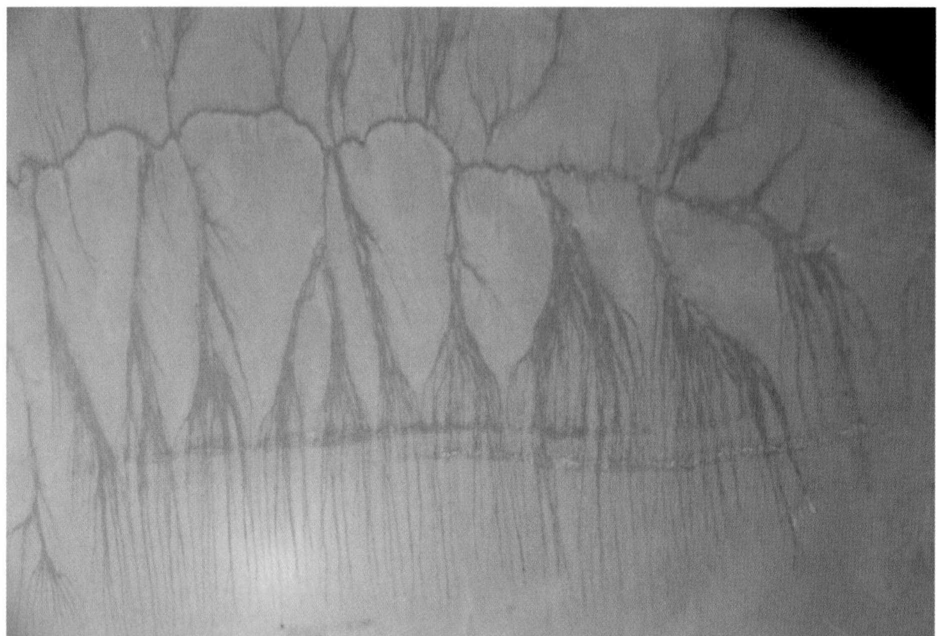

Figure 11.17 Multi-branched waterways in the Alaskan tundra. Notice the bright spot at the bottom, caused by the opposition effect discussed in Section 5.4 (FAI–BRW, 11 July 2012).

Figure 11.18 Airplane and wind turbines seen from the air (MCO–SLC, 30 May 2013).

Figure 11.19 Vivid colors on Maui (SEA–OGG, 21 July 2010).

Figure 11.20 Fading fall colors in the Wasatch Mountains (STL–SLC, 1 Oct. 2013).

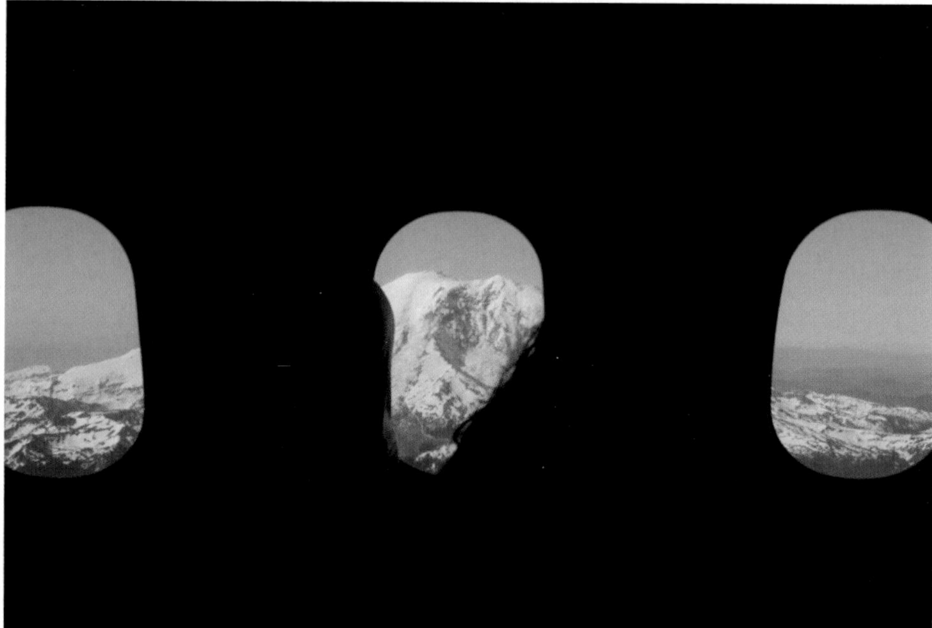

Figure 11.21 Sometimes the best scenery is out the other side of the airplane, as in this view of Mt. Rainier seen through three airplane windows across the airplane aisle (BZN–SEA, 11 July 2012).

Figure 11.22 Please do not be so wrapped up in your work that you ignore the incredible sights just outside your airplane window (BZN–PDX, 16 July 2014).

Appendix
Airport Codes

To help the reader envision the scenes shown in this book, each photo caption includes the airport codes for the flight segment on which the photo was obtained. This appendix provides a list of cities that correspond to the provided codes.

Code	Airport Location
ABQ	Albuquerque, New Mexico, USA
AMS	Amsterdam Airport Schiphol, Netherlands
ANC	Anchorage, Alaska, USA
AGP	Malaga, Spain
ATL	Atlanta, Georgia, USA
BNA	Nashville, Tennessee, USA
BUR	Burbank, California, USA
BRW	Barrow, Alaska, USA
BWI	Baltimore–Washington International, Maryland, USA
BZN	Bozeman, Montana, USA
CDG	Charles de Gaulle, Paris, France
CTS	New Chitose, Sapporo, Japan
DCA	Washington, D.C., USA
DEN	Denver, Colorado, USA
FAI	Fairbanks, Alaska, USA
FRA	Frankfurt, Germany
FUK	Fukuoka, Japan
HND	Haneda, Tokyo, Japan
HNL	Honolulu, Hawaii, USA
ITO	Hilo, Hawaii, USA
JNU	Juneau, Alaska, USA
KOA	Kona, Hawaii, USA
KOJ	Kagoshima, Japan
LAX	Los Angeles, California, USA
LGA	LaGuardia, New York, New York, USA
MCO	Orlando, Florida, USA
MEX	Mexico City, Mexico
MSP	Minneapolis–St. Paul, Minnesota, USA
OGG	Kahului (Maui) Hawaii, USA

PDX	Portland, Oregon, USA
PHX	Phoenix, Arizona, USA
ROC	Rochester, New York, USA
SAN	San Diego, California, USA
SDF	Louisville, Kentucky, USA
SEA	Seattle, Washington, USA
SFO	San Francisco, California, USA
SLC	Salt Lake City, Utah, USA
STL	St. Louis, Missouri, USA
TLV	Tel Aviv, Israel
TUS	Tucson, Arizona, USA